COMMUNICATING TECHNICAL INFORMATION

A Guide to Current Uses and Abuses in Scientific and Engineering Writing

RATHBONE

COMMUNICATING
TECHNICAL INFORMATION

COMMUNICATING

▲
▼▼ **ADDISON-WESLEY PUBLISHING COMPANY**

3 ᵧ

ROBERT R. RATHBONE

Department of Humanities
Massachusetts Institute of Technology

TECHNICAL INFORMATION

A Guide to
Current Uses and Abuses
in Scientific
and Engineering Writing

READING, MASSACHUSETTS · PALO ALTO · LONDON · DON MILLS, ONTARIO

Second printing — June 1967

FOREWORD

In recent years, engineers and scientists have been given so much advice on how to improve their writing that by now they must be either completely confused or completely enlightened. Clearly another book on the subject can be justified only if it lessens the confusion without diminishing the enlightenment.

This book has a modest function: to serve as an inexpensive self-improvement guide for engineers and scientists, whether on the job or in the classroom. The text concentrates on matters that technical people themselves have found to be the most bothersome in the reports, texts, and articles they read day after day. Many points were suggested to me by my fellow teachers in the engineering and science departments at M.I.T. Not only were these people disturbed by the bad writing of some of their students but they also were highly critical of much of their own professional literature. The incentive to publish this book evolved from my discussions with them.

The last chapter in the book offers practical suggestions for the technical person who finds he has to edit the writing of others. It is also intended to advise the writer of his responsibilities and to acquaint him with what he may rightly expect from an editor.

In writing this book, I have used numerous bits of illustrative material borrowed from others. A few words in print is a small price to pay for them. That I owe much more is undeniable; yet the best I can do is to acknowledge my debt by thanking the following: John B. Bennett, Joseph Bicknell, Lynwood S. Bryant, John Fallon, Peter Griffith, Samuel J. Mason, Walter McKay, James B. Stone, Volta Torrey, and Joseph N. Ulman, Jr.

June 1966   R. R. R.
Cambridge, Massachusetts

CONTENTS

1

It isn't that engineers and scientists

can't write — they just prefer to

carry on a peaceful coexistence with

the English language.

OBSERVATION BY AN M.I.T. STUDENT

THE PEACEFUL COEXISTENCE

Let's begin by being realistic: you wouldn't be reading this book unless you wanted some help with your writing. And although you may not be particularly enthusiastic about the project, the fact that you have made the step — even grudgingly — is important.

It is important because it is a start and because you have taken the initiative. It will not work wonders, however. You will have to do more than just read about writing — you will have to *write, write, write,* and you will have to rid yourself of any notions and habits that may have stymied you in the past.

This introductory chapter is intended to help you inspect yourself as a writer and to suggest ways to improve your approach before you begin your next writing assignment. The portraits of writer-types used for this purpose are caricatures; no writer could possibly possess all of the vices described!

You're really not that bad! If you have a lingering phobia about writing — a sort of *horror scribendi* — and hope that "something will turn up" so that you won't have to commit yourself, look at it this way. No one likes to do something he doesn't do well (or *feels* he doesn't do well). But there is no reason to believe that you aren't capable of becoming a competent writer. Engineers and scientists can produce effective writing if they have sufficient motivation and are given proper instruction. As proof, their journal articles on the whole are better written than those of many other professional people. Their reports are even lucid compared with those of professional educators and psychologists.

What you must face, however, is that open hostility toward writing will harm you, and thus your career. You will have to learn at least to coexist with what you may now look upon as a necessary evil. Report-writing as yet cannot be relegated to a computer; it still is an integral part of the human factor in every technical investigation. Peaceful coexistence, therefore, is better than limited warfare: you may soon find that relations improve as tensions disappear and that you actually begin to like writing!

TRY TO PLAN AHEAD

To the outsider, it seems odd that engineers and scientists, schooled in an orderly approach to problem-solving, should have trouble with expository writing. There probably are numerous reasons for their difficulty, but I believe this to be basic: they seldom plan a writing assignment with the same care that they put into planning the technical end of a project. This is true even when the report that comes out of the project may be the only tangible evidence they have to show for their efforts.

If you identify yourself with this problem, try to divide your writing job into easy-to-handle tasks. It has been said, and rightly, that when you have something to write, the first thing to do, paradoxically, is to resist the urge to sit down and write! A writing assignment is a practical problem in communications. Its inputs are not bunched at one point in time, but occur throughout the life of the investigation. It therefore does not make sense to handle all of the writing tasks in one gigantic (and often exhausting) effort at the end. Many of these tasks can be accomplished more efficiently during the project, when information is fresh and motivation is high.

- The audience can be identified and its needs established.
- The problem can be defined and the purpose of the investigation stated.
- The general organization and format of the report can be determined.
- Decisions can be reached on security classification and distribution.
- Information can be evaluated as it is gathered.
- Graphic aids can be roughed out.
- The bibliography can be prepared.
- An outline can be submitted to an editor or colleague for comment.
- Drafts can be written concerning work completed.

As you can see, most of these tasks represent decisions that you, the writer, must make before you begin to write. You will have enough to do later on.

AVOID BECOMING A STEREOTYPE

Technical writing is functional writing, not a form of fiction. Yet it often appears to the reader that some authors handle their papers as though they were writing a mystery story. They withhold a few pertinent facts, they include extraneous information, they report false leads, they build up undue suspense, and they leave questions unanswered. In short, some writers give the impression that the reader should be made to work things out for himself!

Another group of authors would lead us to believe that when a professional person writes something it must *sound professional* (whatever that is). Unfortunately, they interpret this to mean that technical writing cannot be natural, straightforward, personal, or easy to read. The pronoun "I" is outlawed, the passive voice supplants the active, the indefinite "it" occupies key positions in the syntax, and short sentences become long paragraphs.

Still others are firmly convinced that every writer is committed to producing a model of scholarly prose. A scholarly work deserves scholarly treatment. But the advocates of this line sometimes use style simply for style's sake. They choose words to impress rather than to inform. They include innumerable footnotes and references (some that are unnecessary, others that should be part of the text). They tailor the message to fit the syntax, not the other way around. They construct a massive bibliography. And before they know it, the whole thing becomes an exercise in one-upmanship rather than an act of communication.

And finally, there are those who believe that terseness is next to godliness. They have a special talent for brevity, but in their desire to be efficient they frequently sacrifice both clarity and readability. They mean well; they're earnest, hardworking fellows — liked by everyone except their readers. The following satire depicts what happens to an art form (and could happen to writing) when efficiency is carried too far. I wish I knew who the author was. He deserves extra plaudits.

How to Be Efficient, with Fewer Violins

The following is the report of a work study engineer, a specialist in method engineering, after a visit to a symphony concert at the Royal Festival Hall in London:

> For considerable periods, the four oboe players had nothing to do. The numbers should be reduced and the work spread more evenly over the whole of the concert, thus eliminating peaks of activity.
>
> All the twelve violins were playing identical notes; this seems unnecessary duplication. The staff of this section should be drastically cut. If a larger volume of sound is required, it could be obtained by electronic apparatus.
>
> Much effort was absorbed in the playing of demi-semi-quavers; this seems to be an unnecessary refinement. It is recommended that all notes should be rounded up to the nearest semi-quaver. If this were done, it would be possible to use trainees and lower-grade operatives more extensively.
>
> There seems to be too much repetition of some musical passages. Scores should be drastically pruned. No useful purpose is served by

4

repeating on the horns a passage which has already been handled by the strings. It is estimated that if all redundant passages were eliminated, the whole concert time of two hours could be reduced to twenty minutes and there would be no need for an intermission.

The conductor agrees generally with these recommendations, but expressed the opinion that there might be some falling off in box-office receipts. In that unlikely event, it should be possible to close sections of the auditorium entirely, with a consequential saving of overhead expenses, lighting, attendants, etc. If the worst came to the worst, the whole thing could be abandoned and the public could go to the Albert Hall instead.

Economy of speech usually is to be commended. On the other hand, unless a writer realizes that *more words are necessary to convey a thought than simply to express it,* he is apt to indulge in false economy. Don't take "the obvious" for granted. Identify constants in formulas, specify the units in which data are presented, tell the reader what assumptions you are working under. Follow difficult passages with short summaries and provide transitional material that will take him smoothly from one idea to the next. You can read between the lines, but he can't.

OVERCOME YOUR INERTIA

For most people, getting started with any major piece of writing means overcoming human inertia, and unfortunately there is an abundant supply of it in all of us. One suggestion I have heard on the problem came from John B. Bennett, editor of the *Journal of Engineering Education* and guest lecturer at many of the M.I.T. summer programs in scientific and engineering writing. His answer to the question, "How does one get started?" was "Just start!" He was not being facetious, he explained, but simply reminding the group of Newton's First Law: "A body in motion tends to remain in motion; a body at rest tends to remain at rest." "Just start" is perhaps as good advice as any. Say something — anything that will put you in motion. You can throw the top away later if you wish.

John Fallon, director of technical writing and library services of the electronics system division of Sylvania Electric Company, takes a different tack. He suggests that you "bring a friend into your office. Buy him a coffee, loosen your tie, light his cigarette, and start talking: 'Charlie, I'm going to tell you about a computer I just designed. It's a beauty — small, compact, lightweight, economical. We are making it for the Navy. Our only problem now is to iron out the tape-transport.' . . . 'Hold it, hold it,' says Charlie. 'How small is it? How lightweight? What branch of the Navy are you building it for?' A few minutes invested in such a dress rehearsal will give you the talking points for your report and show you where you are not accurately anticipating your reader's questions.''

Perhaps you have heard some of your friends claim that using a dictating machine or tape recorder solves the starting problem. I believe it does help many writers, and recommend that you give dictation a try to see if you and the machine are compatible. Practice by beginning on some short pieces. If you then feel at ease with the system, dictate a report. Outline the entire report first and have good notes to talk from so you won't have to search for things to say. Once you are no longer conscious of the hardware (or the software, if you are using a stenographer), dictation enables you to concentrate on the story. You have no time to worry about grammar and punctuation or to search for synonyms. Consequently, you transcribe your thought into prose quickly and with natural transitions.

A curious but helpful suggestion for producing a rough draft of a long report — one that cannot be completed in a single sitting — is to stop in the middle of a section or a paragraph rather than at the end. When you resume the job (whether you are dictating or writing longhand), you then have enough starting energy built in to go right on without a struggle. Presumably, once you are in motion, new material will come faster and easier. Nonsense? Perhaps, but if your car battery were worn out you wouldn't think it silly to park on a downgrade!

Of course, the biggest roadblock to getting started is not being ready to write — not knowing where you are going. If you know you have nothing to say, but insist on saying it, then you are beyond help. If, however, you believe you're ready but wish to check to be sure, ask yourself these questions:

- What was the objective of my investigation?
- Does the evidence I have gathered or the results I have achieved meet this objective?

If the answer to the second question is yes, jot down the main steps that connect the objective to the solution. You are then ready to fill in the details for an outline. If the answer is no, examine the reasons why you have not met the objective. Are they clear? Unbiased? Logical? Consistent? Credible? Reasonable? An unqualified yes here also means that you are ready to communicate your thoughts to others.

6 .

Suggested Readings

These books are not on the subject of writing, but they do exemplify good writing. They are also enjoyable and informative. Try one in your spare time.

SULLIVAN, WALTER, *We Are Not Alone: The Search for Intelligent Life on Other Worlds.* New York: McGraw-Hill, 1965. Mr. Sullivan is science editor of the *New York Times.*

WIENER, NORBERT, *God and Golem, Inc.* Cambridge, Mass.: The M.I.T. Press, 1964. This book won the 1964 National Book Award in the category of Science, Philosophy, and Religion.

Great Essays in Science, edited by Martin Gardner. New York: Washington Square Press, 1957. The collection contains articles by both modern and classical authors. A "best buy" at 60 cents!

Scientists as Writers, edited by James Harrison. Cambridge, Mass.: The M.I.T. Press, 1965. A sampler of scientific writing of yesterday and today. Demonstrates that basic scientific concepts are comprehensible to the general public if they are presented in a clear, well-written form.

2

It is surprisingly easy to acquire the

usual tricks of poor writing. . . . If the

proposed title, for example, means

something to you, stop right there,

think no further. If the title baffles

the reader, you have won the first round.

THE PRINCIPLES OF POOR WRITING

PAUL W. MERRILL

THE TENUOUS TITLE

In creative writing, authors often use titles to amuse, to challenge, to puzzle, and even to fool their audiences. But the author of a technical report cannot play games with his readers; they want to be informed, and expect to learn something from the first input, the report's title.

There also are practical reasons why technical writing must have informative titles. Titles play an important role in the processes of storing and retrieving information; in addition, they help a reader decide how much more attention he should rightly give one communication than another.

The criteria many writers and editors use to evaluate the effectiveness of a title are:

1. Does the title accurately represent the subject?
   (*Is it correct?*)
2. Are the limits of coverage stated (or implied)?
   (*Is it complete?*)
3. Is the language of the title meaningful to the intended audience?
   (*Is it comprehensible?*)
4. Has the title been expressed as efficiently as possible?
   (*Is it concise?*)

Only a few titles meet all the criteria; the majority miss at least one. Much of the time the violation is not justifiable.

DEADWOOD IN TITLES

Length is no guarantee of precision or clarity in a title. Many of us have the habit of throwing in familiar phrases that add to the word count but not to the information content of our titles. All too often, we follow a common weakness of many professional people: we use a worthless convention simply because it is established in the literature and sounds impressive.

These are some of the overworked phrases that regularly appear at the beginning of titles in technical writing:

A Report of . . .	*An Analysis of* . . .
A Study of . . .	*A Discussion of* . . .
An Investigation of . . .	*A Consideration of* . . .

Note that all these expressions specify in general terms only. They are bad on three counts: they occupy a strong position in the title, yet they are of no use in a literature search; they usually state the obvious; and they invariably lead to further wordiness and vagueness. "A report on" might logically be followed by some such phrase as "the use of" (both of which are unnecessary):

A *Report on the Use of* Water as the Liquid Propellant in Project Transport

Or the opening "an investigation of" could easily tempt a writer to follow with "the effects of," which in turn introduces "using":

An Investigation of the Effects of Using Water as the Liquid Propellant in Project Transport

These examples only slightly exaggerate the danger. Once a writer is trapped by his opening words, he inevitably begins to run off in all directions, piling phrase upon phrase. The title below is from an actual report; for obvious reasons the author will remain anonymous.

The Results of a Study of Investigating the Effects of Using Stereographic Analysis in the Determination of the Lattice Relationships in an Iron-Nickel Alloy

You can appreciably reduce deadwood in your titles by challenging any phrase that describes what is strictly a reporting or information-gathering function.

Borderline Cases

Phrases that sharpen or refine the basic words in a title may often help the reader and should therefore not always be discarded. Test the title with and without the qualifier. If the title makes sense alone, keep it that way. Consider these examples:

TITLE: A SURVEY OF REPORT-WRITING METHODS IN INDUSTRY

Comment: "A survey of" is not necessary to the meaning; the rest of the title implies it.

TITLE: A PRELIMINARY REPORT ON PROJECT BLUNDERSTONE

Comment: "Preliminary" is informative, but "report" is redundant. Handle the phrase either as a separate label designating a type of report (the way "Progress Report" is often handled) or place the phrase at the end of the title.

REVISION: PROJECT BLUNDERSTONE: A PRELIMINARY REPORT

TITLE: AN INTRODUCTION TO INDUSTRIAL DYNAMICS

Comment: "An introduction to" is justifiable in a title, especially in a book title. It announces that the text is for the beginner. But it would be wise to subordinate these words as a "pre-title" by setting them in a smaller type face and keeping them on a separate line.

REVISION: An Introduction to   (pre-title)
           INDUSTRIAL DYNAMICS   (main title)

VAGUENESS IN TITLES

Some writers are vague in their titles without knowing it; others know they are vague but for one reason or another don't do anything about it. Since vagueness obscures meaning, in a title as elsewhere, no author can have a strong case for advocating it.

Examine the following titles. Is the vagueness justified?

TITLE: A METHOD FOR MEASURING POROSITY COEFFICIENTS

TITLE: A SYSTEM FOR IMPROVING COMPUTER RELIABILITY

Comment: "A method" and "a system" are both vague. The titles describe in a general way what the reports are about, but specific words naming the method and naming the system (particularly the principles involved) would make these titles much more meaningful to the reader.

NEW TITLES: MEASUREMENT OF POROSITY COEFFICIENTS BY THE SHALLOW-BORE METHOD

PREVENTIVE MAINTENANCE: AN AID TO COMPUTER RELIABILITY

We can all learn something about improving the wording of our titles from a good news editor. In checking the leads and headlines to stories, he makes sure that the wording is keyed to the theme. He would never accept the vague expression "the effect of," for instance. Yet this expression appears day after day in titles of engineering and scientific writing. Behold:

TITLE: THE EFFECT OF ROLLING UNSTABLE AUSTENITIC STEEL AT 300°C

Comment: The news editor isn't the only one who would object to this title. Any reader would ask, "What is the effect?" I see no reason why words that describe it could not be used.

One reason for the popularity of "the effect of" (and synonymous phrases) is that a precise substitute usually requires the services of a verb — and many writers feel that verbs are too outspoken in titles. Consider these examples:

TITLE: THE EFFECT OF INCREASING THE INPUT VOLTAGE ON THE OPERATION OF THE OLSON ELECTRONIC SWITCH

This title does not even imply what "the effect" is; most technical people, however, would gasp at the idea of changing to:

NEW TITLE: INCREASING THE INPUT VOLTAGE *IMPROVES* THE OPERATION OF THE OLSON ELECTRONIC SWITCH

Does the use of the verb sound odd to you? Perhaps you can see the logic of it in a more familiar subject:

STANDARD TITLE: THE EFFECT OF THE USE OF FERTILIZER ON LAWNS
REJUVENATED TITLE: FERTILIZER HELPS LAWNS GROW

Would you not agree that if we can reflect the theme of our writing in the title, without introducing gee-whiz terms or inaccuracies, we should do so? Verbs are not always necessary. A noun synonym frequently will work, as shown in the earlier example:

PREVENTIVE MAINTENANCE: *AN AID TO* COMPUTER RELIABILITY

SINGLE-WORD TITLES

Single-word titles are satisfactory only for pieces of writing that develop broad or general coverage of a topic. They are frequently seen in magazine and journal articles and often are very effective in drawing an audience. They should not be used in formal technical writing, however, if the subject is limited to a particular segment of a larger topic.

TITLE: LASERS

Comment: All types? The operation of? The design of? The uses of? The title is apt if all aspects are covered, even superficially, but otherwise it is too vague.

TITLE: DESIGN CHARACTERISTICS OF THE X-100 AIRCRAFT

Comment: Shortened to "Characteristics of the X-100" or simply to "The X-100," the title would not be as meaningful.

The rule of thumb is that the more restricted the area of the investigation, the more words will be required to describe it adequately in the title.

TWO-PART TITLES: THE WISE COMPROMISE

If you find that spelling out a topic produces a long, cumbersome title and you are sure it is not crowded with worthless phrases that could be eliminated, you might try the option of a two-part title. The words form a continuous title line separated in the middle by a colon. Ahead of the colon is the main idea; following the colon is the qualifying idea. The new arrangement places the key words first, giving emphasis to the general subject; at the same time, it isolates the qualifiers and thus points out their special significance. In a way, it's like having your cake and eating it too.

Examples

TITLE: HOW REACTION MOTORS WORK AND SOME EXPERIMENTS WITH THEM

Comment: This title is awkward and weak; elements interfere with each other.

REVISION: REACTION MOTORS: HOW THEY WORK AND SOME EXPERIMENTS WITH THEM

Comment: The key words appear first (helpful certainly to the person who must catalog the report); the wording after the colon qualifies and does not interfere.

TITLE: THE PURPOSE AND ORGANIZATION OF THE BOSTON PLANNING BOARD

REVISION: THE BOSTON PLANNING BOARD: ITS PURPOSE AND ORGANIZATION

Comment: In the original, the key words appear in 7th, 8th, and 9th place, respectively. This is not a serious loss in emphasis, but illustrates what would happen if a longer series of qualifiers preceded them.

Titles also can be split physically into two parts, known as the main title and the subtitle. The main title is usually printed in boldface type or caps and is located top center on the page; the subtitle appears below in a less eye-catching format. This convention, which is found regularly in magazines and journals, is also perfectly acceptable for technical reports.

Examples

MAIN TITLE: WHAT SALT DOES IN YOUR BODY

    Subtitle: Salt helps keep the blood neutral, distribute water, and enable the muscles to function properly.

MAIN TITLE: HEAT TREATING CAST GOLD ALLOY

    Subtitle: Heating to 450°F produces optimum hardness and uniformity.

HEADINGS AS SUBTITLES

The headings most frequently found in formal technical writing serve as labels for the standard divisions of a report. The following are typical:

Introduction	Discussion of Results
Method and Equipment	Conclusion and Recommendations
Tests	Appendix
Results	

Without these organizational headings the reader would be lost. But it is often possible to increase their function by changing to words that describe the content more specifically. Instead of "Introduction," for instance, you might use "History of Project Asan"; instead of "Method and Equipment," you might say "Computer Analysis of Wind Tunnel." If you handle your headings as subtitles, *they will inform as they organize.* Try it.

Examples from the Experts

Finally, here are some titles that demonstrate the rules. There really are many excellent ones in our technical literature.

"Proof that the Earth Moves"	(Galileo)
"The Orderly Universe"	(Moulton)
"Blubber into Oil"	(Melville)
"Human Ecology: A Problem in Synthesis"	(Sears)
"Digital Information Storage in Three Dimensions, Using Magnetic Cores"	(Forrester)

And on the lighter side:

"The Last Shall Be First"	(Describing automation in the shoe industry; from Arthur D. Little's *Industrial Bulletin*)

3

Mankind is learning things so fast

that it's a problem how to store

information so it can be found when

needed. Not finding it costs the U.S.

over $1 billion a year.

HOW TO COPE WITH INFORMATION

FRANCIS BELLO

THE INADEQUATE ABSTRACT

In its report on the responsibilities of the government and the technical community in the communication of technical information,* President Kennedy's Science Advisory Committee urged all authors to accept more responsibility for effective information retrieval. Traditionally, the committee pointed out, individual writers have felt concerned only with the initial generation of a document and not with its subsequent dissemination. This separation of tasks must be bridged, the committee continued, and each author can help if he supplies a meaningful abstract with every manuscript which he submits for publication.

At about the same time, but in no way associated with the committee's action, the Westinghouse Corporation published the results of a study of what management wants and reads in technical reports. All the persons interviewed in the study said that they always read the abstract in a report. In contrast, only a few said that they also consistently read the body.†

The above references illustrate but two of the reasons why abstracts are important in technical communication. There are many more. Unfortunately, when the technical man shifts from being a reader to being a writer, he sometimes loses sight of this importance. The result is an inadequate abstract, hastily conceived and poorly directed.

Abstract or summary? Many abstracts are inadequate because the authors are not sure what the design and operational specifications for an abstract are. Inspect any number of references on technical writing and you will find that authorities are not consistent in describing what an abstract is, what a summary is, and whether the terms are synonymous or whether they designate entirely different elements of a report and should therefore be used selectively.

Since the confusion results from a problem in semantics and from personal choice of terms, we shall use only "abstract." Unlike the summary, the abstract appears apart from, and ahead of, the text. It is more of a "sampling" device than a review device. In conjunction with the title, it tells the reader what the main thoughts of the report are; he can then decide whether or not he wants (or needs) to read the details that follow in the body.

---

* "Responsibilities of the Government and the Technical Community in the Transfer of Information," Science Advisory Committee. Washington, D.C.: U.S. Government Printing Office, January 1963.

† "What to Report," *Westinghouse Engineer*. Westinghouse Electric Corporation, Pittsburgh, Pa., September 1962.

TYPES OF ABSTRACTS

The abstract performs its service to the reader in one of two ways:

1. It acts as a *report in miniature*, a capsule version of the main report, highlighting the main points.

2. It acts as a *prose table of contents*, indicating the main topics that are covered in the body.

Some textbooks refer to the report-in-miniature type as "informative abstracts" and the table-of-contents type as "descriptive abstracts." These terms, however, also confuse many writers, since the informative abstract contains technical descriptions and the descriptive abstract can be said to inform. Perhaps some of the confusion can be avoided by substituting "indicative" for "descriptive"; the table-of-contents type "indicates" what the report contains.

The method characteristic of each type can be illustrated by comparing two abstracts of the same report, entitled:

THE M.I.T. ELECTROSTATIC MEMORY TUBE

Example of Informative Abstract

The M.I.T. Digital Computer Laboratory is developing an electrostatic memory tube that will store binary-coded information at two stable potential levels, 100 volts apart. A 2000-volt electron beam "writes" a coded binary digit as a charged spot at any one of 400 positions on a 4 x 4 inch target. A 100-volt electron flood retains stored information indefinitely. Access time is 25 microseconds. Future developments should increase reliable storage density to 1024 binary digits and access speed to 6 microseconds.

Example of Indicative Abstract

This report describes an electrostatic memory tube being developed by the M.I.T. Digital Computer Laboratory for storing binary-coded information in an electronic computer. Details of design and operation of the tube are given and future developments that will increase access speed and storage density are discussed.

Other distinguishing features of the two common types also are apparent in the examples:

- For a given piece of writing, an informative abstract will run slightly longer than an indicative one.

- An informative abstract follows the style and language of the original; an indicative abstract uses passive verbs such as "are described," "are given," and "are discussed."

- An informative abstract often contains much quantitative information; an indicative one does not.

Which type of abstract is preferred? Neither type of abstract is recommended for *all* communications. Make your selection first by analyzing the nature of the subject matter and then by establishing the objective of the reader.

An indicative abstract can be written from almost any type of communication; an informative abstract, on the other hand, is not that flexible. For example, it is not suitable for a textbook or for any long and involved publication. There would just be too many significant points to abstract. Nor is it satisfactory for covering material in which understanding each point of text depends on understanding the point that preceded it (such as in the development of a theory or in an elaborate set of instructions). The informative abstract is at its best with shorter technical communications (report or article length) in which the reduction of text from original to abstract does not have to be so great. Reports on tests and experimental investigations lend themselves nicely to the informative abstract, as do reports that answer "how much?" or "how many?"

If the nature of the subject matter rules out the informative type of abstract, then use the indicative. However, if the subject matter does not eliminate the informative, determine which type will better satisfy the needs of the reader.

The informative abstract is preferred by readers who wish to get the main points (such as results, conclusions, and recommendations) *without* reading the report itself; by those who must take action on the main points immediately but who will eventually read the report; and by those who wish to know special technical details without having to commit themselves to reading the full report.

The indicative abstract is preferred by readers who wish to know what the general coverage of the writing is, what the subdivisions are, and how the material is developed. Perhaps I should say "acceptable to" rather than "preferred by" these readers, because an informative abstract might satisfy them even more if it provided coverage of contents while it reported the main facts.

The indicative abstract is a general-purpose device, so to speak, and should not be used when a special-purpose device will do a better job. *Failure of the writer to make this distinction is the main cause of inadequate abstracts.*

PROCEDURE FOR SELECTING PROPER TYPE OF ABSTRACT

A hypothetical communication situation involving the M.I.T. memory tube can be used to illustrate a simple procedure for selecting the proper type of abstract.

Step 1. *Determine the nature of the communication.* Let us assume that the communication is a technical paper on development work. It is 15 manuscript pages, contains quantitative information, and presents specific results and conclusions. Although theory is outlined, the emphasis is on technical details.

Step 2. *Determine whether an informative abstract is ruled out.* An informative abstract is not ruled out by the length of this paper (15 pages) nor by the treatment of subject matter.

Step 3. *Determine reader preference.* Since both types of abstract are eligible, choice should be based on which one the reader would prefer. If we assume that the intended readers are specialists in designing memory devices for computers, we know that they would be interested in details and in getting quantitative information as rapidly as possible. These facts make selection of the informative abstract mandatory.

Suppose that the communication situation were different. Suppose that the paper were to be published in a technical journal and that the intended readers were electronics engineers from many fields. The analysis might be revised as follows:

Step 1. Technical article, 10 pages of manuscript. More explanatory theory and fewer technical details, but emphasis still on hardware.

Step 2. Informative abstract not ruled out.

Step 3. Reader would prefer the indicative abstract over the informative abstract (as they are written in the examples) because many of the technical details are meaningless to him out of context.

But this suggests that the choice is for the lesser of two evils, and readers deserve better treatment. What about combining the best features of each?

21

Example of Combination Abstract

The M.I.T. Digital Computer Laboratory is developing an electrostatic memory tube for storing binary-coded information in an electronic computer. Present storage density is 400 binary digits; access speed is 25 microseconds. Details of design and operation of the tube are discussed; future developments will increase storage density to 1024 digits and access speed to 6 microseconds.

The reader now has four significant bits of information that he did not get from the straight indicative abstract: the present and projected storage density and access speed of the new device. These are the most important design criteria in a computer memory system, and the reader has the data at a cost of very few additional words.

In brief, write a straight indicative abstract only if the length and/or treatment of subject matter rules out the informative type. Whenever both types are eligible, write either a straight informative type or a combination type, depending on the needs of the intended reader.

WHAT ABOUT LENGTH?

Everyone agrees that an abstract should be short. But how short? Some company style manuals suggest a maximum of one page of abstract for every thirty pages of text. This is not an unreasonable ratio, and serves as a useful yardstick. However, if followed religiously it often encourages inefficiency.

Instead of planning by ratio, you should make every effort to keep *all* abstracts from running over one-half page or 150 words. Naturally, a few may need to be longer if the informational needs of the reader are to be met. But the majority will easily fit within the 150-word limit. In fact, many will not need to be longer than 75 words.

Extremely short abstracts (one or two sentences) raise questions of justification. If the text is short, is an abstract necessary? Can't the reader get the information just as easily by skimming the text? Probably he can, but we still need the abstract to assist in information retrieval.

If an abstract merely repeats information already given by the title, should it be retained? No. It should be rewritten. Consider the title and abstract as forming a communication unit and behaving much as a paragraph. The title, in effect, announces the topic; the abstract develops the topic. The whole has unity, transition, and movement; any redundancy that remains is purposeful.

The convention of confining abstracts to one paragraph often leads to extreme overcrowding. If the material will be easier to read in two or three short paragraphs rather than one long one, there is no good reason for observing the convention.

SUGGESTIONS ON LANGUAGE

All abstracts have a high density of significant words, but all need a few noninformational or "service" words to make the reading easier. Don't forget to supply transitions, especially after taking whole sentences bodily from the text.

The time to establish the key words of your communication for the reader is in the title and the abstract. These words are the nouns and verbs that name, define, and describe the important ideas in your writing. They are the words that would permit accurate filing, referencing, and retrieval of your report. Use standard terms whenever possible; a *Thesaurus of Engineering Terms* has recently been published (1964) by the Engineers' Joint Council. (Their address is 345 East 47th Street, New York, N.Y. 10017.) This is an expensive volume, but your library might be willing to buy it.

Be consistent in the use of technical terms: use the same term in the abstract as in the body.

All but the most familiar abbreviations and acronyms need to be spelled out at first appearance. "NASA," for example, is sufficiently well known to stand by itself; "DCC" (Document Control Center) is not.

It is safe to assume that the abstract of a report, paper, etc., will never appear without the main title. Awkward redundancy between the title and the first sentence of the abstract should be avoided. Here is an example:

TITLE: DIGITAL SIMULATION OF RANDOM VIBRATIONS

First sentence of abstract: This thesis describes an investigation of digital simulation of random vibrations.

The first six words of this sentence are worthless; the remaining five do not contribute any new information. The needless redundancy would never have occurred had the writer thought of the title appearing directly above the abstract (as it does on an abstract card).

MECHANICAL AIDS

There is an unwritten convention within the technical community that warns writers not to use graphic illustrations in abstracts. Undoubtedly this came about because of limitations on the space assigned to abstracts and also because many abstracts are published separately, some on abstract cards. But is it wise to rule out illustrations entirely? They certainly could be used in reports that do not go beyond the family, so to speak, provided they are kept simple and provided they do not make the abstract occupy more than one page. I think you will agree that, had the writer of the abstract on page 19 included the sketch shown in Illus. 3–1, the reader would be able to visualize the unfamiliar device with much more assurance. If you believe that a sketch or diagram would make your next abstract clearer (and if you know you won't be breaking any house rules), go ahead and try one.

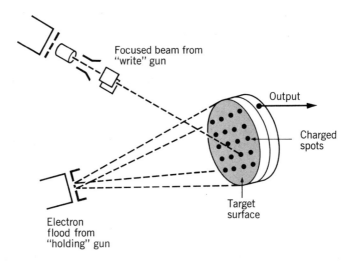

Focused beam from "write" gun

Output

Charged spots

Target surface

Electron flood from "holding" gun

Illus. 3–1. Simplified diagram of operation of electrostatic memory tube.

Subheadings can also be used in abstracts more than they are. There certainly is no law forbidding their use in abstracts. Granted, they may be overdone and they would not be in order in the majority of cases. But they too should not be ruled out categorically; the abstract of the moment is always the important abstract, and it just might benefit from the improvement of organization that a few subheadings would provide. (Remember, of course, that you cannot often use a lone subhead. You must have two at least.)

THOUGHTS ABOUT COVERAGE

Abstracts should be written *after* the main body of the communication, not before. The original communication will thus shape its own image, and not vice versa.

The abstract should never contain information not presented in the body of the report.

A well-written, informative abstract is a replica, in miniature, of the original. It, too, has a beginning, a middle, and an end, with emphasis on the key ideas and/or results.

Most writers outline their material before they write the first draft. The enlightened ones also prepare a statement of thesis which they use as a guide for selecting and rating the raw material they have collected during the investigation. This statement of thesis relates the initial problem and objective to the subsequent results and conclusion. It prescribes the course of development the author wishes his message to take in order to communicate successfully with a specific audience. Reduced to its key words, the statement of thesis will form a meaningful title; expanded with supporting details, it will form a meaningful abstract. Chapter 4 discusses how to establish and develop the statement of thesis as a writer's tool.

In conclusion: Here is an abstract that is both *informative* and *indicative,* not to mention *revealing.* It was written by a student after he attended a lecture on brevity and honesty in report-writing.

Abstract

As the reader would discover anyway, this report has no new results to offer. It should prove useful, however, as a means of reviewing what the project group has been doing for the past six weeks.

4

If your writing falls apart, it probably has no primary idea to hold it together.

THE PRACTICAL STYLIST

SHERIDAN BAKER

THE WAYWARD THESIS

Problems, Problems! Scientific and engineering investigations begin with a problem; most of the time they end with a solution. But the way is not always clear. The investigator frequently runs into secondary problems that demand so much attention that he loses sight of the real reason for his involvement.

There is a story of an electrical engineer who was assigned the job of obtaining some data on pulse behavior in a computer circuit. Before he could begin his testing, he had to design special test equipment; this took a month. He then had to supervise the construction of the equipment and to check it out. These items took another month. To obtain the requested data, however, took only three days. In his report on the project, the engineer used 30 of the total of 36 pages to describe the design and construction of the test equipment. To him, this was the important information; he had spent practically all of his project time obtaining it. Yet this information was *not* of primary concern to the person receiving the report. As a result, the whole report had to be reorganized, material dropped, and the emphasis shifted to the solution of the original problem — the problem that brought about the investigation in the first place. The moral of this story is that much time may be wasted if the writer does not first distinguish primary information from secondary information, and then shape his communication accordingly.

FIND A THESIS

Just as an engineer or scientist needs an hypothesis to guide him in conducting an investigation, so a writer needs a statement of thesis to guide him in *reporting* an investigation. He needs something that will enable him to determine which course of action out of the many available to him is the best suited for a given communication.

As mentioned at the end of Chapter 3, the statement of thesis is a writer's tool. It is an internal communication from the writer to himself before he begins the writing job. It is a mental communication, at least initially, and may be formed even before the investigation is completed. It tells the writer what the intent, general coverage, and emphasis of his communication should be. Without it, many writers suffer from "writer's block" or, as John Bennett of the American Society for Engineering Education puts it, from *"thesis paresis."*

ANATOMY OF THE THESIS

A statement of thesis is a statement of "aboutness." It answers the question "What *about* the subject?" For instance, "Transistors are more rugged, require less power, and occupy less space than vacuum tubes" is one possible statement of the aboutness of transistors. "Although its cost is higher, process A produces a more reliable component than process B, and therefore should be adopted" concerns the aboutness of process A.

As the two examples show, a statement of thesis expresses an opinion. It is the writer's appraisal of the significance of his subject. However, he does not necessarily have to express this opinion verbatim in the written text. Often he prefers to let the facts speak for themselves.

Whether included as part of the text or not, the statement of thesis does represent what the writer hopes the reader will gather as being the central idea of the writing — what he hopes will be the main thought that the reader will carry away with him when he finishes the reading. Certainly there is a good chance of the reader getting the idea the writer has in mind if the writer forms the idea into a thesis first and then organizes his material around it.

The statement of thesis can also suggest how to organize the subject matter in a report. Here is an example.

STATEMENT OF THESIS

The X-100 aircraft meets all of the USAF specifications for performance, structure, and instrumentation.
(Note: The statement answers the question "What about the X-100?")

GENERAL ORDER OF MATERIAL

I. *Performance:* Specifications, tests, results, evaluation

II. *Structure:* Specifications, tests, results, evaluation

III. *Instrumentation:* Specifications, tests, results, evaluation

NEW REPORT: NEW THESIS

From a single investigation there can spring many communications, each with a different audience and a different intent. Thus coverage and treatment of the subject must be determined for each new reporting situation. For example, the first communication to come out of an investigation might be addressed to an audience interested primarily in test procedure and results; later a second communication might be issued to a different audience interested only in the economics of the project. In each case, a statement of thesis prepared in advance of the actual writing would tell the author what priority to assign to

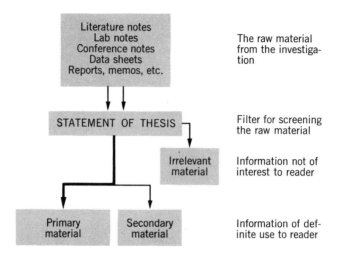

Illus. 4–1. Using the statement of thesis to screen material for a report.

each segment of information he has collected. In effect, the statement of thesis serves the author as a filter for selecting which material is relevant for his report and classifying it as primary or secondary. Illustration 4–1 depicts this important function.

Case Study

This brief study illustrates one way of avoiding a wayward thesis.

Company X manufactures bulk chemicals. During the summer months, it has trouble protecting flammable liquids stored in its tank farm. All the tanks have standard protective devices, yet disastrous fires still occur.

Company Y manufactures an auxiliary system for protection of volatile liquids stored in above-the-surface tanks. You work for Company Y. You have talked to the management of Company X and are convinced that your equipment will solve their problem. Your assignment now is to write a report convincing them.

You begin organizing your thoughts by forming a tentative statement of thesis:

Our equipment can solve their storage problem *because* it greatly reduces the fire hazards introduced by high atmospheric temperatures and electrical storms.

You examine this thought for a moment and realize that you will have to support it. So you revise the statement to include technical details:

By introducing inert gas into the vapor space and by cooling the skin of the tank with water, our system will reduce by 90% the fire hazards caused by high atmospheric temperatures and electrical storms.

You decide that this version correctly represents the central idea you wish to present in detail as the main body of text. It expresses the aboutness of your protection system in relation to Company X's problem.

Your next step is to determine what information your readers will need if they are to accept your thesis. You realize that they will want to know immediately whether you really understand their problem. This thought prompts you to plan an introductory discussion of their equipment, the liquids they store, and the reported causes of their accidents. You also realize that they will wish to know what the costs of installation and operation will be; you decide, therefore, to follow your description of the system with a section on costs. These decisions on content make sense to you because your case depends on Company X's acceptance of the premise that the new system will work.

In summary, your thinking about an appropriate thesis and how you should support it has, in a very few minutes, provided you with a general outline of your report. You are now ready to screen your source material and to set up a working outline.

STATEMENT OF COVERAGE

It is not possible to state a thesis for all types of technical writing. Straight expository prose — writing in which no side is taken or no opinion offered — is better served by a *statement of coverage*. Operating instructions, descriptions of how to assemble something, and simple laboratory reports are typical cases of such statements.

The statement of coverage, like a statement of thesis, is a device to help the writer. It is formed before the writing begins so that it will provide a sense of direction. It is an informal statement, sometimes written out, sometimes not.

Unlike the statement of thesis, it is definitive rather than argumentative. It focuses on things themselves rather than on ideas about these things. It takes no line one way or another about the subject. It represents the author's opinion only as to how the subject is to be explained and how the explanation is to be organized.

Except, perhaps, for the term, there is nothing new about a statement of coverage. But in their flush of enthusiasm to get the job done, inexperienced writers frequently bypass preparatory steps that experienced writers take automatically. Collecting one's thoughts about the coverage of the subject is perhaps the most important of these. Often this simple maneuver can save an otherwise worthless piece of writing.

5

Trying to explain a new scientific

theory without first introducing its

general character and purpose is like

trying to entice a woman to make

love by winking at her in the dark:

the intent never is realized.

NORBERT WIENER

IN A CONVERSATION WITH THE AUTHOR

THE IMPROPER
INTRODUCTION

In questioning several groups of college students recently on whether they were having difficulty writing their B.S. theses, I was not surprised to find that about a third reported trouble with the Introduction. This figure is not a general statistic, of course, but it does reflect a problem that often arises whenever engineers and scientists have major writing jobs to do.

The main reasons the students gave for having trouble with the Introduction were:

1. Don't know exactly what an Introduction should do for the reader.

2. Don't know how to determine what the reader already knows.

3. Don't know how to organize the material effectively.

The order in which these causes are listed is not intended to indicate a priority; one cause of trouble can be as damaging as the next. Let us briefly consider each of these stumbling blocks.

THE INTRODUCTION AND THE INTENDED READER

A quick way to understand what an Introduction should do is to examine it in relation to the communication as a whole. The introductory section supplies preliminary material to help the reader quickly understand and appreciate the real message that the communication carries. Its role is to bridge whatever gap may exist between the writer and his audience so that the purpose of the communication can be fulfilled.

The gap is primarily one of information. For example, if a reader is to understand why a certain procedure was followed in a research project, he will need to be briefed on the problem that brought about the project. A proper Introduction would provide the information he needs, no more but certainly no less.

The gap may also be one of motivation. The reader may need to be prodded, challenged, or otherwise stimulated to read. When this is the case, the Introduction acts in the same way as the lead in a magazine article. Working closely with the title, it builds up reader interest in the "story." If it is well written, it does this simply and honestly, never promising anything the author can't deliver.

In short, an Introduction in technical writing is designed to prepare the intended reader intellectually and emotionally for the serious job of interpreting and evaluating a message.

DETERMINING WHAT THE READER ALREADY KNOWS

If the intended reader (i.e., the primary audience, whether one person or many) has a technical background similar to yours, he will need at least as much briefing about the assignment as you did. Remember, you are at the end of the investigation; the reader is at the beginning. Think back to the time you were assigned the work. What briefing were you given? What questions did you ask? What preliminary investigating did you have to do? What information did you discover later on that would have helped you more if you had found it earlier? Your own needs can serve as a reliable gauge.

If the intended reader has a technical background in a specialization other than yours, you will have to carry your questioning a step further. What explanatory information in addition to that required by the first audience will be needed? This question has no pat answer, but most of the time the supplementary material involves definition. The common ground of writer and reader is now restricted to their general technical knowledge. To expand this ground so that the reader will be able to understand the specialized aspects of the communication, you will need to define many terms and concepts that did not need defining for the previous audience. As these special items appear in the Introduction, relate them whenever you can to something that is already known and thus familiar to the reader. Handle your descriptions in as simple, concise, and straightforward a manner as possible. You can check on your judgment by asking someone with a background similar to the intended reader's to comment on what you have written.

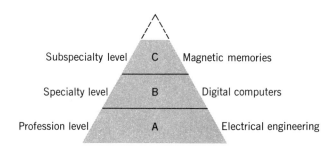

Illus. 5–1. Levels of reader context.

Illustration 5–1 outlines the process of coordinating the technical level of the subject with the background level of the reader. The electrical engineering profession is used as the guinea pig. The bottom block of the pyramid,

A, represents the technical knowledge common to everyone in electrical engineering. It naturally has a broad base and includes many people. The second block, B, represents the added knowledge common to everyone in a specialty of electrical engineering, digital computers. It includes fewer people. Block C represents the highly specialized knowledge common only to those involved with magnetic memories.

Suppose that an engineer in the C-group has just finished investigating the operating characteristics of a new magnetic material and is asked to report his findings. If his report is to go to magnetic-memory specialists, like himself, he need only introduce his communication within the context of C. If, however, the report is going to computer engineers specializing in areas other than magnetic memory, he should introduce his communication within the context of B. Should the audience be electrical engineers, but in radar work, say, rather than computers, the Introduction would have to be formed within the general context of A.

Any writer can work out a pyramid profile of his reader, compare it with his own profile to see which blocks they have in common, and then use the highest of these as the context within which to introduce his subject.

ORGANIZING THE INTRODUCTORY MATERIAL

If the Introduction is to help the reader, it must follow some organizational pattern that will carry him from the familiar to the unfamiliar, from the general to the specific, from doubt to open-mindedness. One way to accomplish this development is to invert the pyramid, as in Illus. 5–2.

The apex of the pyramid, now at the bottom, represents the special subject to be presented in the report. The base line above represents the broader area of context from which the reader's preliminary understanding of the subject must be drawn. The development involves closing in on the subject through one or a series of logical steps. The number of steps required depends on the length of the base line, the highest level of context in which the writer and reader meet.

A single step usually is sufficient when the writing is addressed to fellow specialists. One common pattern is the problem-solution sequence. The problem explains the "why"; the solution, the "what." Illustration 5–3 is an example.

More than one step may be desirable to introduce the same subject to a wider technical audience. Illustration 5–4 shows how this can be done.

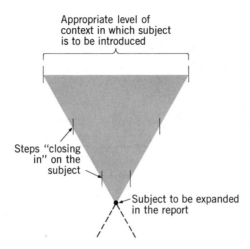

Appropriate level of
context in which subject
is to be introduced

Steps "closing
in" on the
subject

Subject to be expanded
in the report

Illus. 5–2.   Inverted-pyramid technique for developing the Introduction.

THIN-FILM TRANSDUCERS

Westinghouse has developed a method of producing transducers that will vibrate at ultrahigh frequencies but not shatter under their own vibrations. The technique involves depositing a thin film of cadmium sulfide from vapor in a vacuum chamber onto a substrate . . .

Illus. 5–3.   Example of a single-step introduction.

THIN-FILM TRANSDUCERS VIBRATE AT ULTRAHIGH FREQUENCIES

Piezoelectric transducers, which convert electrical pulsations into mechanical vibrations, ordinarily consist of a thin wafer of a crystalline material such as quartz. To achieve high frequencies, these ordinary piezoelectric crystals must be made so thin that they shatter under the vibrations they generate; they are so fragile, in fact, that it is nearly impossible to handle them without breakage.

A new way of making crystal wafers produces transducers that are much more durable. These transducers have been operated at frequencies up to 75,000 megacycles, and the technique should eventually provide frequencies approaching a million megacycles.

The transducers are thin films of cadmium sulfide deposited on a substrate from vapor in a vacuum chamber. . .

Illus. 5–4.   Introduction expanded for a wider audience. (From *The Westinghouse Engineer,* November 1964, **24,** 6, p. 192.)

Another familiar pattern is the problem-purpose sequence. Here a statement of the problem exposes an underlying cause that produces a general undesirable effect; the purpose relates the immediate investigation to the cause-effect problem. Illustration 5–5 is an example of this sequence.

PROPOSAL FOR INSTRUMENTING A BLIND MAN'S CANE

A cane still is the best inanimate mobility or guidance device available to the blind person. It is easier to use and is more reliable than any of the existing sonar or optical scanning and detecting devices that have been developed during the past twenty years.

It is not known why a cane works as well as it does; nor have all of the useful stimuli it provides the user been evaluated. Development of a better device, therefore, cannot be expected until the job of evaluating the cane's performance is completed.

The purpose of this investigation will be to measure all of the physical variables that the cane produces and to correlate these with the user's responses so that the relative importance of the stimuli can be established.

Illus. 5–5.   Example of problem-purpose sequence (from a student's report).

Some writers prefer to begin with a statement of purpose, following with the statement of problem. Their reason for the preference is that the reader is informed immediately of the objective of the investigation. The reason is valid and the pattern is acceptable. But there are some disadvantages:

- Transition from Introduction to Body is not as smooth.

- Motivation cannot be built up as effectively.

- Awkward redundancy sometimes exists between the title
  and the opening of the Introduction.

These negative effects can be somewhat lessened if the impact of the purpose is held to the end by dividing the statement into two parts. The opening would explain the purpose in terms of a general solution. This would be followed by a detailed statement of the problem. The close would restate the purpose in terms of the immediate objective of the investigation.

Not all Introductions can be developed smoothly in one or two steps. The reader may need to be informed of many things — some historical, some technical, some political. Where the emphasis is placed will depend on the reader's background and present interest. Illustration 5–6 provides a good example of a multistep Introduction.

The common danger of a long Introduction is that the reader will lose interest and quit. To lessen the chance of this happening, writers should never assemble the Introduction into a single, many-page paragraph. Instead, they should see if the material might not be divided conveniently into logical parts (the steps of the pyramid). Each part might be a paragraph or, if there is a great deal to say, a group of paragraphs tied together by a heading. The reader is thus given some freedom of movement and can skim if he wishes. (Another scheme, of course, is to relegate some of the details to an appendix.)

WHAT SALT DOES IN YOUR BODY

A homespun philosopher once said, with more sense than syntax, "Salt is what makes things taste terrible when you forget to put it into them." Evidence archeological, documentary, and anthropological shows that all peoples have always prized salt.

Existing remains of salt mines have been dated authentically to the late Bronze Age, about 1000 B.C. As early as 400 A.D. the Chinese drove salt wells to deposits over a half mile below the surface. Salt availability more than any other factor originally drew dense populations to the valleys of the Jordan, the Nile, the Tigris-Euphrates, and the Yellow River of China. Peoples of pre-colonial Africa concentrated along the coast, where sea salt is plentiful. A sprinkling of tribes in the interior then depended (as some still do) on animal blood and urine for salt. Indigenous populations in pre-Columbian Mexico were mostly in the southern sections, where there are natural salt deposits.

Although salt is cheap, its sources are so limited that its supply may readily be controlled. Oppressive governments through the ages have contrived monopolies and imposed heavy taxes on salt. Such policies were a principal catalyst of the French Revolution. Gandhi's organization and direction of the famous salt march to the sea are considered to have been his crowning efforts towards Indian emancipation.

But is salt a true physiological need, like the human requirement for other minerals such as calcium or for such vitamins as ascorbic acid; or is salt a "comfort" or luxury, like alcohol, tobacco, tea or coffee? The answer turns out to be: Some of both.

Illus. 5–6. Example of multistep introduction. (From an article by Frederic W. Nordsiek in *The Technology Review*, April 1965, p. 25.)

To conclude: Readers need and want an introductory section in their reports, but don't enjoy reading any more preliminary material than is absolutely necessary. Writers can trim the Introduction to fit their readers' needs by beginning their account at the proper level of context and then closing in on the subject by a series of logical steps. Some Introductions have to be long because a great amount of historical background is needed to bring the reader up to date. In these cases, length can be made less objectionable if the material is divided into sections and headings used.

If, after you've worked awhile on polishing your Introduction, you still don't like the way it reads, remember that many an Introduction has blossomed after the opening paragraph was lopped off!

6

Any ambitious scientist must, in self protection,

prevent his colleagues from discovering that

his ideas are simple . . . So if he can write his

publications obscurely and uninterestingly

enough no one will attempt to read them but all

will instead genuflect in awe before such erudition.

MATHMANSHIP

NICHOLAS VANSERG

THE ARTFUL DODGE

In this age of scientific marvel it may be unfair (and even unpatriotic) to accuse scientists and engineers of double-talk or intentional hedging. But this is not to say that they never confuse or mislead when they write a report. The verbal haze commonly found in their writing can produce the same result unintentionally.

Unfortunately, confusion is not the only serious consequence; there is always the danger that the reader who is misled will think the writer is pulling an "artful dodge" just to save his own skin. Such a reaction usually spells disaster for the communication.

Fortunately, any writer can avoid giving the false impression that he is hedging if he observes a few simple rules of common sense. This chapter discusses those rules.

THE VEILED INSULT

No writer wants to insult his audience, intentionally or unintentionally. Yet one of the quickest ways to achieve that result is to tell the reader that something is *obvious* or *clear* — when to him it isn't obvious or clear at all. Repeated often enough, the ruse can succeed in frustrating him completely.

The following examples represent typical cases:

It should be obvious from the foregoing description that resonance is achieved through direct gamma-ray interactions.

As we can clearly see, the factorial design makes very efficient use of the information in each run and reveals the presence of interaction between factors, each based on a variety of experimental conditions.

The reaction of the input module is clearly demonstrated in the second set of equations.

It is clear from the data that further investigation will be unnecessary.

Although the tests were inconclusive, it is clear that the overall project was a success.

If something is obvious, there's no need to say so; *if there's a chance it isn't obvious,* why insult the reader by saying that it is?

Along the same line, some mathematicians like to save time by substituting the word "hence," for a page or two of intermediate calculations. This short-cut in itself isn't bad, but if the calculations are never included or are relegated to an obscure appendix without any mention in the text, the reader quickly develops an inferiority complex when he tries to bridge the gap. Don't force your readers to accuse you of deliberately trying to mislead them!

Sometimes writers are in such a hurry to finish a piece of writing that they can't resist shifting all responsibility for technical description onto graphic aids. "A picture is worth a thousand words," they remind themselves, and then quickly send the reader to Figure 1 for "details of how the system operates." Some graphic aids are intended to supplant words, but others can only supplement them. When both a verbal and a graphic description are needed, be sure to include both. The reader can quickly detect whether a drawing, photograph, or curve should be supported by text matter. Unfortunately, he can't do anything about it if the words are missing.

Finally, be careful about telling the reader that something can be clearly seen in an illustration. Let *him* draw that conclusion. I remember writing that the controls of a certain piece of equipment could be *clearly* seen in a photograph. They were clear in the original glossy print all right, but not in the copy that finally appeared in the published report!

THE MEANINGLESS QUALIFIER

Qualifiers are designed to sharpen the words or expressions they qualify. When, however, the qualification cannot be visualized accurately or consistently, the audience can easily be misled.

Consider this statement: "The cost of the project should be *well under* a million dollars." How much is "well under?" $750,000? $10,000? $1.00? The qualification cannot be visualized in any meaningful way. (This is fine if you want to fool the audience, but not if you want to convince them.)

Suppose we reword the above statement: "The project will cost between $700,000 and $900,000." Although the dollar spread is wide, this revised statement is meaningful, and no reader would now accuse the writer of having an ulterior motive!

The expression "etc." can mystify a reader for hours if it appears at the end of a series of unrelated items. Not knowing what comes next, he can only hope for the best. Suppose you received the following telegram:

HOME BROKEN INTO LAST NIGHT — STOP — DOG, JEWELRY, MONEY, ETC. MISSING.

You probably would rush home in a hurry — worried, naturally, about your money, jewelry, and dog, but also concerned about the "etc." What could it be? Your doctoral dissertation? Your wife?

The mystery can be just as confusing in technical writing. "Etc." is meaning-less if the reader cannot complete the missing items of a series:

To build the component, we shall need a rag, a bone, a hank of hair, etc.

Be specific. Don't use "etc." to cover up laziness or lack of information or to mislead the reader into thinking that there are more items than there actually are. Reserve it for those instances in which spelling out the series would in-volve the reader unnecessarily:

Match the pairs as follows: No. 1 with No. 7, No. 2 with No. 8, No. 3 with No. 9, etc.

The *floating comparative* is also a villain, yet may look innocent enough at a casual glance. It is the qualifier without a referent. We say that something is "faster" or "longer-lasting" or "more economical," but forget to complete the comparison. Thus we can have a legitimate referent in mind, but the reader may think he is being given a sales pitch. Tie down the comparative and you will avoid this embarrassment.

The adverb *relatively* is another troublemaker. It is commonly used in such expressions as:

a relatively high temperature   or   relatively expensive equipment.

The word is meaningless if the reader does not have a standard on which to base the qualification. It therefore must be defined for anyone not versed in the conventions of the subject being reported. "A relatively high temperature," for example, means one thing to someone working in pyrogenics; another thing to someone in cryogenics.

Other types of vague or meaningless qualifiers found in technical writing are:

a great many	considerably	very
more or less	mainly	rather
to some degree	reasonably	little
by and large	nearly	largely
a number of	appreciably	generally

After questioning one of my students recently as to what he meant by the term "reasonably sure," I received this amusing explanation: " 'Sure' con-veys no information by itself. It serves merely as a convenient point from which to express varying degrees of certainty. Each expression has special significance to the engineer." He then wrote the following list on the board.

44

Not quite sure
Fairly sure
Rather sure
Reasonably sure
SURE
Very sure
Real sure
Sure indeed
Sure as hell

E. B. White in the book, *The Elements of Style,** calls the qualifiers *very, rather,* and *little* "leeches in the pond of prose, sucking the blood of words." I included them in the above list because these qualifiers are used to qualify other qualifiers, and thus can doubly confuse the issue. If we could see ourselves in print as we see others, we would never be caught saying:

a *very thorough* investigation	a *rather deadly* poison
a *very timely* occurrence	a *little more* difficult
a *rather dangerous* experiment	a *little less* frequent

If we jolted ourselves sufficiently, we might even see the wisdom of using an unadorned, unqualified phrase.

An IBM booklet on writing a technical paper† offers the following passage to illustrate the evils of over-qualifying. The unnecessary words are italicized.

This study, *which is as yet inconclusive,* supports the theory, *within pre- scribed limits,* that the apparent, *though yet unmeasurable,* loss of iron from ferrite, *though in no other observable composition,* is due, *to the best of our knowledge,* to the atomization, *or what might thus be termed,* of Fe_2O on the cation points.

THE VAGUE REFERENCE

Most of you correctly follow one of the several accepted procedures for writing footnotes and compiling a bibliography, so these procedures will not be reviewed here. But you frequently violate the principles of documentation

---

* Strunk, William, Jr., and E. B. White, *The Elements of Style.* New York: Macmillan, 1959.
† From "So You're Going to Write a Paper," copyright 1958 by IBM Corporation, Yorktown Heights, New York.

in statements that you make as part of the text. Here is an example of what I mean:

> It is believed that engineering colleges should hire more scientists as teachers.

This statement is both vague and dishonest. Who believes it? The impersonal "it" construction takes in the whole technical and academic community! Here is another:

> The literature shows that rain in Spain falls mainly in the plain.

Undoubtedly certain sources show this, but the reader is not helped if you casually cite all the literature as your authority. To him, you are taking unfair refuge behind a professional cliché.

And finally, here is a list of approaches, any one of which might easily destroy reader confidence:

> The vast majority of scientists feel that . . .
> (a vague, wordy cliché)

> These figures, all from reliable sources, indicate . . .
> (a political runaround)

> A number of people have asked why . . .
> (any number is "a number"; also, what people?)

THE HIDDEN ANTECEDENT

Paul W. Merrill* has suggested that an easy way to catch the reader off guard is to use a pronoun to refer to a noun which was mentioned a long way back, or to use a pronoun to stand for something not directly expressed. "If you wish to play a little game with the reader," Merrill continues, "offer him the wrong antecedent as bait; you may be astonished how easy it is to catch the poor fish."

The pronouns that cause the most trouble in technical writing are "it" and "this" (and their plurals). They can easily become vague when the text contains two or more possible antecedents and the sense of the message does not tell the reader which one is the right one.

---

* Merrill, Paul W., "The Principles of Poor Writing," in The Scientific Monthly, January 1947.

VAGUE "IT"

If the gate brackets the signal of interest and if the amplitude of this signal has any frequency dependence, *it* will be recorded at the console.

(Can you name the hidden antecedent?)

VAGUE "THIS"

The preceding method provides an easy understanding of the so-called stress-relieving effect of closely spaced grooves and notches. *This* will now be illustrated.

(What will be illustrated: the method or the effect?)

The authors of the two examples could easily have saved their readers from grief if they had repeated the appropriate nouns instead of using pronoun substitutes.

EUPHEMISMS AND WEASEL WORDS

Euphemisms are expressions substituted for ones that suggest something un-pleasant, i.e., *pass away* for *die*. They are popular with writers when failures or setbacks have to be reported or when the results of an investigation are not as expected. Students writing lab reports, for instance, are all too familiar with the old saw:

The experiment reflected uncertain results.

(*Meaning:* The experiment failed.)

The practice is not restricted to the classroom, however. The following description from the *Style Manual* of the Aerojet-General Corporation* points out that senior citizens also succumb.

Reporting Failures or Setbacks

One of the most difficult tasks for the technical writer is the adequate, yet prudent, discussion of disappointing results obtained in a program.

The most common mistake is to attempt to gloss over failures or set-backs. It is natural for an engineer to be optimistic about his work and to minimize difficulties. However, this tendency must not prevail to the extent that the reader is misled (or thinks that an attempt is being made to mislead him). Nothing can destroy a reader's confidence more effec-tively than the feeling, justified or not, that the writer has tried to deceive

---

* Reprinted by permission of Aerojet-General Corporation, El Monte, California 91734.

him. Any attempt to belittle difficulties will create a bad impression. The report writer will do better to present a frank discussion of the difficulty and then proceed to a logical analysis, followed by a discussion of the steps taken to deal with the problem.

The following examples of "weasel words" would not be likely to impress a critical reader favorably:

1. "Three tests were conducted and all firings were very successful except the third, during which a malfunction occurred . . . damaging the unit beyond repair."

2. "Six tests were run and the firing curves were very smooth for all except the first, third, fourth, and sixth."

3. ". . . a pressure surge occurred. A search for the missing parts was initiated."

4. ". . . a major nonfiring occurred."

5. ". . . divergent instability developed."

6. ". . . a rapid structural failure occurred."

It is also possible to carry frankness too far, as in the following example:

"Although instruments of different manufacture, but comparable quality, from those discussed herein might be substituted, to do so would entail, in some instances, extensive changes in this report."

HEDGE WORDS

Close cousins to euphemisms and weasel words are hedge words — words and phrases that the writer feels let him off the hook, so to speak. They come in all shapes and sizes and are excellent for any writer who wishes to develop a noncommittal style.

The amateur begins with the common "possible," "probable," or "perhaps," but soon graduates to the more sophisticated "it would seem that," "it is likely that," or "the data indicate that."

The professional knows no bounds:

So far as we know, the design specifications for the X-100 are more rigid than those for the X-99.

The results are as reliable *as the time and equipment allotted to the project would allow.*

All the evidence *seems to point to the conclusion that* a renewal of the contract will be necessary.

The data *may be considered reliable until such time as new evidence is uncovered.*

But, you say, you like your job and want to keep it. What then? Well, you can avoid going out on a limb and still satisfy the reader if you will observe this simple *and reasonable* rule:

At the outset, state clearly all the specifications, bounds, limits, and assumptions you had to follow in conducting your project and by which you wish it to be judged. Have done with qualifying at once, then state each result, conclusion, and recommendation in as straightforward a manner as you can. You will not be accused of executing an artful dodge.

7

The difference between the right word and the almost-right word is the difference between "lightning" and "lightning bug."

MARK TWAIN

THE UBIQUITOUS NOISE

"Noise" in information theory is broadly defined as any factor within or outside of a communication system that alters the intended message, i.e., the thoughts the originator wishes to convey.

All man-to-man communication systems are susceptible to interference from noise; some systems more than others. But none seems to suffer so much from the effect as writing.

The odds are high against writing a noise-free message because the English language itself is so irrational and because the originator and the receiver have no feedback channel of any kind between them. The reader has no way to influence the transmission and the writer has no way of knowing that he is creating noise.

In a simple communication situation consisting of a writer, a report, and a reader, the elements of the system are as shown in Illus. 7–1. The writer performs three tasks: he gathers the information, encodes it into language symbols, and transmits the symbols as signals. The reader reverses the process: he receives the signals, decodes them into symbols, and interprets the symbols into information.

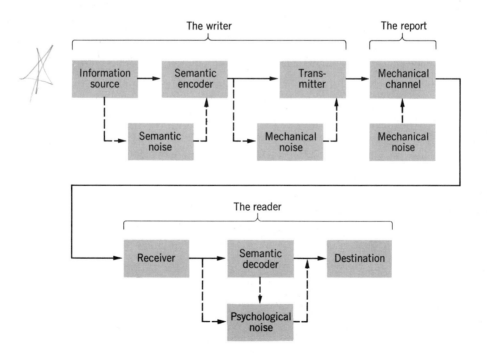

Illus. 7–1. Elements of a simple communications system.

Noise can, and does, occur at each of the three elements: the writer may unwittingly create semantic noise at the encoder or mechanical noise at the transmitter; the report itself may be subject to mechanical noise from numerous other sources; and the receiver is often the victim of psychological noise, the source of which may be the message itself, semantic or mechanical noise in the message, or some external stimulus.

SEMANTIC NOISE

To encode a message in writing, the originator must translate his thoughts into word signals and assemble the signals into message units, such as phrases, clauses, sentences, and paragraphs. To communicate successfully, he must select signals that the reader will be able to retranslate into the original thoughts and he must use a structure that will show the precise relationship the thoughts are to have, one to another. Failure in either of these operations will create "semantic noise."

Every writer does have some control over semantic noise, since he is the one who creates it. But most readers do not expect the amateur writer to be able to control it completely at all times. They *do* expect a favorable signal-to-noise ratio, however — one that permits them to read through the interference easily and to restore the original message. The following techniques, conscientiously applied, are certain to reduce semantic noise to a tolerable level.

Select the right word. The right word is the word that will convey a given thought accurately, clearly, and efficiently to a given audience. What is right for one set of readers, however, may not be right for another. Whenever you have a choice among words, you must base your definition of "right" on the reader's background and knowledge.

Define the specialized word. If a notion has but one word to represent it, the problem is not in word choice but in whether the specialized word needs to be defined. Some technical words are in such common use that they do not need to be explained to the reader. *Voltage,* for example, is a technical word, but the nontechnical person understands it. *Acetylcarboxypeptidase,* on the other hand, is known only to a biochemist and his colleagues. Such a word represents just a large hole in a sentence until the reader knows what it means.

Make the context clear. Many technical words (as well as plain English words) have several meanings. The verbal context in which these words are used must tell the reader which meaning is intended. *Program,* for example, might confuse the reader if it were used first for its special meaning in computer work and then in the next sentence for its common meaning as a plan of procedure. I can recall how much astonishment the term "bus driver" (describing a computer component) caused when it appeared in a paper addressed to a nontechnical audience!

A small point, really not worth arguing about, but isn't it time we stopped using the term "practicing engineer"? The usage may be consistent with the notion of "practicing" a licensed profession, but the term as we generally apply it is not restricted to licensed or registered engineers. Also, the double meaning of "practicing," to me at least, is awkward. Why not follow the sciences in this regard? There are no "practicing scientists," since the sciences are not licensed professions, but there are as many kinds of scientists as there are kinds of engineers, and the scientists get along very nicely without "practicing"!

Prefer the plain word. Plain words create less noise than ornate, formal words because they are known to more people. If a formal word is the exact symbol of what you wish to convey and its informal counterpart is not, then use the formal word — defining it when necessary. But if the plain word represents the image equally well, or better, always prefer it.

Why say this? . . .	if you mean this
utilize	use
terminate	end
magnitude	size
optimum	best
unique	uncommon
conjecture	guess
necessitate	need
fabricate	build

H. W. Fowler, in his *Dictionary of Modern English Usage,* points out that many of our words are "not the plain English for what is meant . . . but translations of these into language that is held more suitable for public exhibition." He calls these words "indoor words" and "outdoor words," the indoor words being "those that the mind uses in its private debates to convey to itself what it is talking about." He insists, however, that most of the time the outdoor words are not needed, and suggests that the less change from the indoor to the outdoor word the better. His reasoning makes sense: the writer thinks of "try" but translates it into "endeavor"; the reader sees "endeavor" but re-translates it into "try."

Be wary of the -ize and -wise suffixes. By the time this book is published the fad of coining words ending in "-ize" or "-wise" may have subsided. Let's hope so. But in case there are still some diehard enthusiasts around, here is a word of caution. Most "fad" words are short-lived. Their potency decays rapidly and those few that manage to survive become clichés. Have you seen an "-ize" or "-wise" expression of recent vintage that was not vague or wordy or overformal or ridiculous or awkward?

-WISE

Our program is ahead of Russia's, *missilewise*.

Weatherwise, the outlook for Boston is rain.

We expect to resolve the problem *computerwise*.

The committee reported that the curriculum needs to be revised *science-wise*.

(Whenever jokes are made about a particular usage, it's a sign that the usage has lost standing. This one came from an M.I.T. freshman: "Two owls who hadn't seen each other for a long time met one night at the local belfry. Said one owl to the other, 'Tell me, Seymour — how are the kids doing, *wisewise*?' ")

-IZE

If Lincoln had had the advantage(?) of the modern -*ize* form, the Gettys-burg address might have had a contemporary ring:

"Fourscore and seven years ago our fathers *functionalized* on this conti-nent a new nation, *conceptualized* in liberty, and dedicated to the propo-sition that all men are *democratized*. Now we are engaged in a great civil war, testing whether that nation, or any nation so *conceptualized* and so dedicated, can long be *firmed up*. We are met on a great battlefield of that war. We have come to dedicate a portion of that field, as a final resting-place for those who here *finalized* their lives. . . ."

The Gettysburg address is a noble and lasting document without a *finalized* jot. Like it or not, though, official Washington has added some-thing that is *homogenizing* the American tongue.

(The above quotation is from the *Boston Herald*.)

Prefer the single verb to the verb-noun combination. Long verb phrases can create noise by distracting the reader from what is significant and by slowing him down. A weak verb-noun combination is a poor substitute for a single strong verb.

Avoid this construction	Prefer this
to make a study of	to study
to arrive at an approximation	
as to how much	to estimate
to take into consideration	to consider
to give some assistance to	to help
to have a particular preference for	to prefer
to conduct an investigation of	to investigate

In their book, *Federal Prose, or How to Write in and/or for Washington*, Masterson and Phillips give some beautiful examples of how a wordy verbal construction can lead to pompous diction:

English	Federal prose
Scissors cut.	Scissors effect scission, functionally.
Hens lay eggs.	Gallinaceous ovulation is effected only by hens.
Haste makes waste.	Precipitousness entails negation of economy.

Place modifiers near the words they modify. If you don't, the reader might think they modify something else and miss your point entirely.

In the neighborhood of the crystal's resonant frequency, Pierre Vigoreaux has derived the following values for the parameters. — J. N. Ulman, Jr.
(Those Frenchmen do get around!)

The student who cheats in the final analysis harms nobody but himself.
(What about the one who cheats in the preliminary analysis?)

Baseball Commissioner A. B. Chandler opened a hearing on charges that Leo Durocher struck and kicked a fan at the Polo Grounds a half hour ahead of schedule today. — J. N. Ulman, Jr.
(Possible, knowing Mr. Durocher!)

The effect of thickness of surface film on friction, metal transfer, and wear has been described as being related to the plastic roughening mechanism in a paper by one of the authors.   (Sandpaper?)

When properly plugged into a circuit, you would expect this meter to indicate the amount of current.   (If you could still read, that is.)

The actual weight of the impellers will vary from that calculated by 50 to 150 percent.   (Calculated by 50%?)

The object of this thesis is to design a solar still that will convert sea water to drinking water on a portable scale.
(In bottles, cans, or on tap?)

Having swollen because of the rain, the workman was unable to remove the bracing.   (Call an ambulance!)

Eliminate roundabout expressions. Words that say things indirectly are always potential sources of noise. A complete list would run into the hundreds. Here are a few of the more common ones.

Wordy	Concise
due to the fact that	because
on account of	because
in the event that	if
in case	if
a large number of	many
a great deal of	much
at the present time	now
despite the fact that	although
for the purpose of	for, to

I have already condemned the vague "it is believed that . . ." in Chapter 6 and would like to indict the rest of the "it" clan now. You will always improve a sentence by dropping the "it" construction.

Original: It is essential that the design specifications be modified.
Revision: The design specifications *must* be modified.

Original: It is recommended that the design specifications be modified.
Revision: The design specifications *should be* modified.

Original: It is apparent that the design specifications were modified.
Revision: Apparently the design specifications were modified.
or
The design specifications were modified.

Original: It can be shown by tests that the higher the speed the greater the rate of error.
Revision: Tests show that the higher the speed the greater the rate of error.

57

Original: It can be seen in Figure 4 that the pulse repetition frequency does not remain constant.

Revision: The pulse repetition frequency does not remain constant (see Figure 4).

or

Figure 4 shows that the pulse repetition frequency does not remain constant.

Taboo: "It is obvious that . . ." and synonymous phrases.
"It is felt that . . ." and synonymous phrases.
"It is needless to say that . . ." (Why say it, then?)

Subordinate secondary ideas. Grammar tells a writer how to shape the appropriate forms to carry his thoughts: put primary thoughts in primary grammatical constructions, secondary thoughts in secondary constructions, and parallel thoughts in parallel constructions. We violate this commonsense rule most often by placing a secondary thought in a primary construction. This is not a cardinal sin, but it may well miscue a reader sensitive to proper English usage. We can easily avoid the violation by carefully watching our use of the conjunction "and."

"And" is a coordinating conjunction; that is, it connects items of equal weight. When used to connect clauses, it announces to the reader that both the clause preceding and the clause following are independent clauses — primary grammatical constructions. If both the thoughts contained in these clauses are not primary, the "and" has been used improperly. The following sentences illustrate this point.

Secondary thought not subordinated: "The results have been summarized in Table 1 and prove that the earlier method was less effective."

Secondary thought subordinated: "The results, summarized in Table 1, prove that the earlier method was less effective."

In the second version, the reference to the table has been relegated to a secondary construction, shifting the emphasis of the sentence onto what the results prove.

MECHANICAL NOISE

Mechanical, or physical, noise assaults the reader from two sources — from the report itself and from the environment in which the report is read. Most forms of environmental noise are well known: loud conversation in an adjoining room, telephones ringing, interruptions by visitors, construction equipment operating in the yard. Environmental noise, of course, adversely affects all kinds of human activities. But it is especially troublesome in written communication because the person responsible for the success of the communication, the writer, can do nothing to prevent its occurrence.

Mechanical noise within the report itself is another matter. The writer is accountable for it, and can control the worst of it if he exerts a little ingenuity and effort. Some of the common forms are given below, with comments on how to lessen their intensity.

Poor quality of copy. This form of noise is serious, but fortunately it occurs infrequently. The main source: stretching the capability of a particular duplicating system in order to meet a deadline. Writers can help by getting their copy to the typist (or publications group) on time.

Overcrowded text. The eye needs white space on a page to relieve the monotonous tramp of solid black lines. Large blocks of text, if continued page after page, produce an adverse psychological effect as well as an adverse physical effect. Variation in paragraph length, indentation, use of headings and subheadings, change in spacing between lines when the structure changes, generous margins on both sides of the text, and vertical listing of points all help to break the monotony and to provide a resting place for the eye.

Inadequate left margin. Many reports are held together by a stiff binding of some sort. If the left margin of text is less than one inch, some of the message can become concealed in the binding. Insist on a one-and-a-quarter-inch left margin, even if your report is to go into a loose-leaf notebook. (Otherwise a three-hole punch may cut into the text.)

Binding too stiff. It is always desirable (and sometimes necessary) for the reader to be able to keep a report open to a certain page without holding it with his hands, turning it upside down on his desk, or applying weights. Losing one's place by having a book or report close suddenly is not a quieting experience. Shop around for covers and bindings; try different types before you order in quantity.

Inadequate labeling of figures and tables. Figures and tables should bear labels that identify their parts, without need of reference to the text. Readers frequently thumb through a report, stopping at the graphic illustrations; they are enlightened only if the illustrations are self-sufficient.

You can diminish noise from this source if you: (1) assign a number to each graphic aid; (2) provide a main title; (3) label all axes, columns, and rows; (4) specify the units in which data are presented; (5) define in a note all special symbols and abbreviations; (6) make curve lines bolder than grid lines; and (7) use as open a grid as will still permit the reader to interpret the data correctly.

Late reference to figures and tables. The reader's attention should be directed to a graphic aid the moment he needs the information it provides. Late reference forces him to reread the text in order to appraise it in terms of the new evidence. If a reference comes very late, the reader may give up before he ever reaches it.

Regarding placement, figures and tables should be located after the reference in text, not before. Nothing is more disconcerting to a reader than to come upon an illustration and have no idea how it fits into what he is reading or to feel that he has missed the reference to it.

Too few headings. Headings act as signposts for the reader: they help him skim, locate the material he needs, and follow the organization of the message as he reads along. Without headings to guide him, he has to rely entirely on paragraphs to accomplish these tasks.

Most inexperienced writers err on the side of too few headings rather than too many. Anything can be overdone, but in general headings are effective antinoise devices.

Typos, spelling mistakes, punctuation errors. These lapses in the mechanics of a piece of writing create noise, sometimes serious noise. I recently found the following typographical error in a technical report: "value" for "valve." It was caused by poor handwriting on the draft (the typist mistook the word) and it changed the entire sense of the passage.

The most common spelling mistakes involve homonyms (sound-alikes). The worst offenders are:

Principle (noun "rule," "basic law") for *principal* (adj. "chief," "foremost")
Forward (verb "to transmit") for *foreword* (noun "front word")
Effect (verb "to cause to happen") for *affect* (verb "to influence")
Continuous (adj. "unbroken") for *continual* (adj. "closely repeated")
Discreet (adj. "prudent," "modest") for *discrete* (adj. "consisting of distinct elements")

Punctuation errors are serious if they create ambiguity; bothersome if they mislead even momentarily. Consistency in usage precludes many from developing. The survivors have to be caught during proofreading. In particular, watch for hyphen omissions in compound adjectives, as in these examples:

Ambiguous: "a new color applicator" (new color or new applicator?)

Specific: "a new-color applicator" (an applicator for applying new colors)

Ambiguous: "a short delay component" (short component?)

Specific: "a short-delay component" (component that produces a short delay)

Ambiguous: "an instant coffee heater" (a device to heat coffee in an instant?)

Specific: "an instant-coffee heater" (a device to heat instant coffee)

A plan of attack. You can wait for proofreading to catch the routine mechanical errors in a manuscript, such as typos, punctuation omissions, and faulty page numbering, but you should not wait to go after weaknesses in format or physical structure. Before you write the draft, determine how the reader will wish to use your finished product. If you are writing a field manual, will it help him if you specify a size that will fit his pocket? Should the printing be made large enough to be easily read in poor light or while he is performing some physical task? If you are compiling a reference book, would the reader be helped if the main sections were tabbed and many subheadings used? In your instruction book, would a single fold-out drawing or separate in-text drawings be better for the intended use? Do you anticipate revisions? If so, would a loose-leaf binding be more practical than a stiff one?

The more mechanical matters you settle early in the writing project the more time you will have later on to concentrate on reducing semantic noise. Procrastination itself breeds noise.

We can also introduce noise when we use the language of mathematics. This is admirably illustrated in the following short satire from *Chemical Digest,* published by Foster D. Snell, Inc.

> Although most of our lives at Snell are spent making complex problems into simple answers for our clients, sometimes we amuse ourselves doing the opposite. We feel that our colleagues in engineering, physics and chemistry spend too much time complicating the simple before they publish their scientific papers. They do this in a great many ways, but the principles can be easiest illustrated by a simple mathematical example. Every paper to be published must above all conform to certain basic precepts whether it is clear or not. Every new chemist

or engineer must learn early that it is never good taste to designate the sum of two quantities in the form:

$$1 + 1 = 2 \tag{I}$$

Anyone who has made a study of advanced mathematics is, of course, aware that:

$$1 = \ln e$$

and that:

$$1 = \sin^2 x + \cos^2 x$$

further:

$$2 = \sum_{n=0}^{\infty} \frac{1}{2^n}$$

Therefore, equation (I) can be expressed more scientifically in the form:

$$\ln e + (\sin^2 x + \cos^2 x) = \sum_{n=0}^{\infty} \frac{1}{2^n} \tag{II}$$

This may be further simplified by use of the relations:

$$1 = \cosh y \cdot \sqrt{1 - \tanh^2 y}, \qquad e = \operatorname*{Lim}_{z \to \infty} \left(1 + \frac{1}{z}\right)^z.$$

Equation (II) may therefore be rewritten:

$$\ln \left\{ \operatorname*{Lim}_{z \to \infty} \left(1 + \frac{1}{z}\right)^z \right\} + (\sin^2 x + \cos^2 x) = \sum_{n=0}^{\infty} \frac{\cosh y \cdot \sqrt{1 - \tanh^2 y}}{2^n} \tag{III}$$

or:

$$\ln \left\{ \operatorname*{Lim}_{z \to \infty} \left(1 + \frac{1}{z}\right)^z \right\} + (\sin^2 x + \cos^2 x) - \sum_{n=0}^{\infty} \frac{\cosh y \cdot \sqrt{1 - \tanh^2 y}}{2^n} = 0. \tag{IV}$$

At this point, it should be obvious to even the casual glance that equation (IV) is much clearer and more easily understood than equation (I). Of course, there are various other methods which could have been employed to clarify equation (I), but these should become obvious once the reader has grasped the underlying principle.

After carefully studying this brief discussion, the neophyte should be better able to appreciate the advantages of these methods when he chances upon them in his reading of the literature. When he has once acquired some facility in the application of these notations, he will be able to write technical reports and papers for publication, the clarity and simplicity of which will surely inspire comment.

But of course we never use these methods in writing reports to our clients.

—Philip A. Crispino*

* Reprinted by permission of Foster D. Snell, Inc., New York.

8

The most dramatic situation, the

lightest humour, the profoundest wit,

the most illuminating revelation of

truth, will fail to reach its mark if the

proper pace has been misjudged.

REGINALD O. KAPP

THE NEGLECTED PACE

Undeniably, pace is an important variable in conveying technical information. But it cannot be defined in quantitative terms, nor can it easily be separated from other communication variables and examined in the laboratory.

In oral communication, pace is the rate at which the speaker presents information to the listener. It is not so much the speed at which he speaks as it is the way he times the important ideas he wants his audience to accept. He paces his talk so that when he presents these ideas the audience is ready for them and will give him their full attention.

In written communication, pace is the rate at which the *printed page* presents information to the reader. It therefore is not directly determined by the speed at which the writer writes (although careful writing often promotes more rapid reading), but it does influence the speed at which the reader reads. As in oral communication, pace controls timing.

The proper pace in technical writing is one that enables the reader to keep his mind working just a fraction of a second behind his eye as he reads along. It logically would be slow when the information is complex or difficult to understand; fast when the information is straightforward and familiar. If the reader's mind lags behind his eye, the pace is too rapid; if his mind wanders ahead of his eye (or wants to), the pace is too slow.

Every reader likes to be able to finish a report as quickly as possible, but a rapid pace does not guarantee rapid comprehension. The writing must be paced so that the reader will be able to understand what he is reading, without having to stop or reread. When a slow pace achieves this timing better than a rapid pace, the reader achieves a better overall reading time.

EXAMPLES OF IMPROPER PACE

The pace in the two examples below has been exaggerated so that the negative effects of improper pacing can be spotted immediately. Both passages were paraphrased from the delightful nonsense article "The Turbo-Encabulator."*

Pace too rapid: The Turbo-Encabulator has a base-plate of prefabulated aluminite, surmounted by a malleable logarithmic casing in such a way that the two main spurving bearings are in a direct line with a pentametric fan constructed of six hydrocroptic marzelvanes so fitted to the

---

* "The Turbo-Encabulator in Industry," by J. H. Quick, in *Student's Quarterly Journal,* Institution of Electrical Engineers, London, 1944.

ambifacient lunar waneshaft that every other conductor is connected by a nonreversible tremie pipe to the differential girdle-spring on the "up" end of the grammeters.

Pace too slow: The operating point is maintained as near as possible to the h.f. rem peak. This is done by constantly fromaging the spandrels. The spandrels are of the bitumogenous type. It is interesting to note that they have a distinct speed advantage over the standard nivelsheave. Also they require no dremcock oil. This is true even when the phase detractors have remissed.

Overcrowding is the fault in the first example. Too many significant bits of information are tied together in a single sentence. The reader is not given time to sort them out and therefore cannot be receptive to new information as it comes along.

The second example has the opposite trouble. There are too many stop-and-go operations and too much drivel between significant points of information.

The next two examples were taken from actual reports. They are in no way exceptions.

Pace too rapid: Since there is a 50 percent probability that the true rank is less than the median rank, the value of the median rank is obtained by integrating the marginal probability density function of the *j*th-order statistic of a random size n using the limits from 0 to nFj and setting this integral equal to the probability P that a random observation will have a rank at or before nFj.

Pace inefficient: The automatic controller receives all the information necessary to control the vehicle. This information is in the form of two signals generated by separate oscillators aboard the vehicle. These oscillators operate continuously at two different audio frequencies.

The first of these excerpts also shows how overcrowding a sentence will produce an improper pace. The density of information is too high for rapid comprehension — even by a mathematician. The single sentence needs to be broken into two parts: one to present the general premise; the other, the details. This simple operation would give the reader enough time to organize his thoughts. The pace in the second example is not so damaging, but if it were to continue at the same rate for much longer the reader would soon tire. Consolidation of the three sentences into one would serve the reader better because it would link the key words to each other more smoothly and rapidly. One such revision might be the following, which says the same thing in half as many words.

The automatic controller receives its information from two different audiofrequency signals, transmitted continuously from separate oscillators aboard the vehicle.

But even a single short sentence can be dangerous if it contains much quantitative data. Watch what happens in the next example. No reader can easily digest more than two or three precise numbers without being permitted to pause, especially if these numbers qualify different units of measure or describe different characteristics.

Overcrowded with numerical data: Experiments showed that the camera had an error of 2 percent of the sampling rate (60 cps) for a 500-watt 13-by-23-degree sealed-beam tungsten-lamp target at 3000 feet.

Pace adjusted: Experiments showed that the camera had an error rate of 2 percent of the 60-cps sampling rate. The target was a 500-watt, 13-by-23-degree, sealed-beam tungsten lamp, located 3000 feet from the camera.

The final example illustrates pace that is too slow even for an instruction manual.

Pace too slow: A handwheel is provided for manual operation of the rotary table. This handwheel is the self-releasing type. When it is engaged, it actuates a switch. This switch disconnects the power clutch in the drive.

Pace adjusted: A self-releasing handwheel is provided for manual operation of the rotary table. When engaged, the handwheel actuates a switch that disconnects the power clutch in the drive.

In the original version, the many full stops and the repetition of key words slow the pace. But deceleration is not necessary; the sentences do not contain any numerical data, the text is not part of a set of instructions, nor are there any unfamiliar technical words or complicated ideas. The simple adjustment shown in the revision allows the reader to move along smoothly and swiftly.

FACTORS THAT GOVERN PACE

You have often heard a speaker say, "Now for a change of pace. . . ." What he really meant was that he was about to change the subject from something serious to something light, from something involved to something simple.

Novelists and dramatists, too, change the pace by changing the subject. They can shift from plot to plot at will — from melodrama to satire, from tragedy to comic relief.

When they change the subject, these gentlemen may also change their technique of delivery. The speaker relaxes and adopts a less formal attitude and tone of voice as he shifts to something light. The novelist quickly changes from exposition to narration to dialogue — to whatever form will best fit the mood of the moment.

Most of these factors that govern pace are not open to the technical writer. He must treat his subject matter as he would his rich maiden aunt. He must be extremely careful about introducing a personal anecdote or a humorous aside. He must be formal and polite at all times. Snappy dialogue is out, gesturing is out, suspense is out, excitement is out, exuberance is out!

What is left? You would be surprised:

- He can change from a statement to a question
  (as in this opening).

- He can vary the length of his sentences and paragraphs.

- He can emphasize important material by placing it in a
  prominent position or prominent construction.

- He can deemphasize secondary material by relegating it to a
  secondary position or secondary construction.

- He can show parallel thoughts by placing them in parallel
  constructions.

- He can relieve difficult text by introducing visual aids.

- He can use analogy.

- He can shift from straight lines of prose to columnar listing.

- He can break up large units of text by inserting headings
  and subheadings.

- He can change the size of type face.

- He can use white space to relieve the eye and/or isolate the text.

- He can modulate his "voice" by underlining, italicizing,
  or by placing his remarks between parentheses.

- He can repeat, and repeat, and repeat.

- And finally, he can regulate his choice of words.

In short, he can adjust the pace through effective control of the most routine elements: sentence structure, paragraphing, punctuation, format, organization, graphic illustration, and word choice.

DETERMINING THE BASIC PACE

Different types of writing — even different types of technical writing — have different basic paces that best suit the purpose and style of the type. Narration is developed historically. Time is the base and a time sequence is easy to follow. There is no trick to the organization; the characteristic pace therefore is rapid. Technical description, on the other hand, may follow any one of a variety of developments and the character of the pace will vary accordingly.

Several types of technical writing and the basic pace normally associated with each are given in the following table.

Basic Pace in Different Types of Technical Writing

Type	Basic pace	Reason
Letter	Rapid	Personal; subject limited
Interoffice memo	Rapid	Informal; subject limited
Abstract	Slow	Facts all primary; crowded
Instruction manual	Slow	Time needed between statements
Historical survey	Rapid	Time as base
Technical report	Slow to medium	Introduction rapid; technical descriptions slow
Mathematical analysis	Slow	Many separate steps

ADJUSTMENT OF THE BASIC PACE

Anyone can determine the proper basic pace by looking at the function and overall method of development of the communication he is about to produce. But all this does is to establish the "right ballpark." He still has much to do if he is to meet his reader's needs: he must decide where in the text the basic pace needs to be adjusted and how the adjustment is to be made.

In an earlier book,* coauthored with James B. Stone, I devised a guide for determining the proper pace for the individual prose units within a piece of technical writing — the sections (or subsections) and the paragraphs. Pace is not a constant, as I have already pointed out; it must vary when the

---

* Rathbone, Robert R., and James B. Stone, *A Writer's Guide for Engineers and Scientists.* Englewood Cliffs, N.J.: Prentice-Hall, 1962.

complexity of the subject matter varies and when the knowledge the reader brings to the subject varies. This guide is based on the answers to two yes-or-no questions:

1. Is the reader unfamiliar with the general area of the subject?
2. Is the subject matter of the prose unit in question complex (detailed)?

I have reproduced the guide here, with the examples that illustrate its use, because I have received many favorable comments on its practical value and have found no better formula to handle the ideas it conveys. The words "normal pace" in the third column refer to the in-between or medium pace most people use in their daily writing.

Guide for Control of Pace

	Subject area unfamiliar?	Subject complex?	Adjustment of pace
Condition 1	Yes	Yes	Begin at slow pace; maintain slow pace
Condition 2	Yes	No	Begin at slow pace; accelerate to normal pace
Condition 3	No	Yes	Begin at normal pace; decelerate to slow pace
Condition 4	No	No	Begin at rapid (or normal) pace; maintain rapid pace

The technique is illustrated in the following examples. Suppose an electronics engineer were writing to a colleague familiar with the general area of pulsed circuits. The subject matter contains many technical details, so Condition 3 exists.

Example 1 — *Pace not adjusted to Condition 3 (familiar but complex)*

The Electronic Computer Division of the Servomechanisms Laboratory has developed a new line of test equipment that will simulate the pulsed circuits of large computer systems. The equipment is designed to operate with positive, 0.1-microsecond, half-sine-wave pulses and a minimum pulse period of 0.5 microsecond, has a standard input impedance of 93 ohms, and may be interconnected to perform the basic operations of a computer.

Example 2 — Pace adjusted to Condition 3

The Electronic Computer Division of the Servomechanisms Laboratory has developed a new line of test equipment that will simulate the pulsed circuits of large computer systems. The equipment is designed to operate with positive half-sine-wave pulses. These pulses must be 0.1 microsecond wide and at least 0.5 microsecond apart. Since all units have the same input and output impedance (93 ohms), they may be interconnected to perform the basic operations of a computer.

In the first example, the pace of the first sentence is good, but the pace of the second sentence is too rapid — even for a colleague. Too many details are crowded together, separated only by commas.

In the second example, these details are spread over three sentences, with but one sentence containing two pieces of numerical data. Separation is especially important when the numbers are precise numbers and do not qualify the same unit of measure. A reader usually can digest only one number per sentence unless he slows the pace or rereads.

THE MECHANICS OF ADJUSTING THE PACE

In the examples at the beginning of the chapter you saw how overcrowding a sentence produced too rapid a pace and how dividing the sentence into several sentences decelerated the pace. You also saw how a series of short sentences produced too slow a pace and how combining certain sentences accelerated it. You will have to call on other techniques, however, as you progress from paragraph to paragraph and from section to section in a report. I have already suggested what these are, but believe that further details on some of the points will help.

Format. "Rest areas" are essential to the well-being of anyone who has to read scientific and engineering reports. These areas customarily are found in two locations: between chapters and between sections. The space between chapters offers the longer break of the two, but the higher frequency rate of the sectional space makes it more important in controlling pace. Unfortunately, this is the space that many writers fail to provide in ample supply.

Headings are the labels for chapters and sections. These handy devices serve a multiple role: they signal the change of thought, they organize the material they govern, they permit the reader to skim, and they act as reference points. The **BOLD CENTERED HEADING** looming above the text has the greatest holding power; the marginal heading, the next; and the indented heading in line with the text, the next.

White space, particularly the amount given to margins and to the distance between lines of print, has a powerful effect on pace. The eye tires rapidly when a dark block of type dominates page after page, and the reader frequently loses his place when the lines are spaced too closely.

Unless they are absolutely necessary, footnotes should be avoided. They interrupt the reader unmercifully.

Paragraphs. Paragraphs are the basic building blocks of technical writing. Any paragraphs over half a page long could run into trouble with pace. Too heavy a concentration of technical information exhausts the reader; he needs relief from paragraph overcrowding just as he does from sentence overcrowding. *A series of overcrowded paragraphs is deadly* — especially if some of the sentences they contain are also overcrowded.

Remember, too, that a short paragraph by itself may be desirable, but that a series of short paragraphs may produce the same undesirable effect as a series of short sentences. It all depends on the length of the series and on the function of the communication.

Most people achieve variety in paragraph length automatically, without devoting special attention to it. So don't spend your time counting words during revision of the draft. Instead, check just for the long series. Six or more short paragraphs in a row or four or more long ones should be challenged.

Sentence structure. Standard sentence order — subject, verb, object — is the easiest to follow and therefore the most adaptable to a rapid pace. This is an added reason for using it frequently.

A short sentence (10 words or fewer) is excellent at the beginning of a passage that will of necessity become involved. It prevents you, the writer, from engulfing the reader on first contact. It is also excellent at the end of a long dissertation, particularly if it summarizes the information in a nutshell.

Don't overlook the power (and the danger) of stating an idea as a question. The device can help the pace and sharpen your style if it is not repeated too often. Also, be sure that you answer any questions you ask.

Wording. Often the space between the end of one sentence and the beginning of the next does not give the reader enough time to understand what he has just read. He then is not receptive to new information when it comes along.

We could give him more time by stretching the physical space — and this we often do by beginning a new paragraph. But some ideas are so closely related that they need to be located side by side. In these cases we have to use another delaying tactic.

I call the technique *strategic use of service words.* These words do not in themselves represent objects or ideas, but show relationship. Transitional words, such as the conjunctions, are service words. So are introductory phrases such as "on the other hand," "in summary," and "in contrast."

To pace our writing so that the reader is ready for an important point, we have to add to the words necessary to express our thoughts those words that are necessary *to convey* them. By including service words ahead of our significant words, we often can stretch the thought period just enough to allow the reader's mind to catch up with his eye.

And finally: I want to return to the author who opened this chapter, Reginald Kapp. In his book, *The Presentation of Technical Information,** Mr. Kapp made this further observation:

> Most of those who have technical information or philosophical argument to present have done little towards solving [the reader's] problems of pace and timing. One hardly ever hears them discuss these problems. I doubt if they know that there are any. So low has the standard of literary craftsmanship sunk in the scientific and philosophical worlds.

Mr. Kapp was not an outsider looking in. At the time he wrote his book he was dean of the faculty of engineering at the University of London and, before that, Pender Professor of Electrical Engineering, University College, London.

---

* Kapp, Reginald O., *The Presentation of Technical Information.* London: Macmillan; first printed in 1947, reprinted in 1957, printed in the United States in 1957.

9

Readers cannot understand information

flung at them [randomly], a chip of geography

here, a piece of economics there, a funny

story tossed in for good (or bad) measure.

Instead, they require that a subject first be

reduced to some understandable scheme. . . .

INFORMATIVE WRITING

JOHN S. NAYLOR

THE RANDOM ORDER

Careful organization of material is the key to a successful scientific or engineering report. To the reader, clear and straightforward order reflects clear and straightforward thinking. A muddled report suggests a muddled investigation — whether it was so or not.

Organization is also important because it bears directly on timing. The order in which information is grouped determines when a reader will reach a specific chapter or section or passage or thought. For this reason alone, organization should never be left to chance.

For the purposes of this discussion, we shall examine organization at two levels: the general organization of the whole communication and the internal organization of the parts. The coverage will be limited to the formal report, since the requirements of organization, style, and format are more rigorous for it than for the informal type.

ANATOMY OF A FORMAL REPORT

Most formal technical reports have three distinct classes of material:

1. The front matter
2. The body
3. The appendix

The front matter consists of special service material. The following items are common:

The cover
The title page
The table of contents
The abstract
The foreword

Not all reports need a foreword, nor is a table of contents necessary if there are fewer than 10 or 12 pages. A few reports substitute a letter of transmittal for a foreword. In such a case, the letter is included right after the title page.

The body is the business end of the report. It corresponds to the chapter coverage in a textbook and contains all the information necessary to satisfy the primary purpose of the communication.

The appendix contains supporting material — material not critical to the understanding of the text but which is of interest (and help) to some readers.

Items that are commonly found in an appendix include the following:

Bibliography

Tabulations of data (included in graphs in the body)

Derivations of equations

Sample calculations

Sample forms used in the investigation

Informative material for the secondary reader:
definitions of terms, descriptions of equipment

Fold-out drawings

Appendix material should not be arranged in random order, but organized in the order in which it is referred to in the text. Any item that the writer suspects will not be of use to his readers should be kept out, no matter how fond he is of it. Reference to appended material should be made at that point in the text where it will be of use to the reader.

GENERAL ORGANIZATION OF THE BODY

The body of every formal technical report should have a beginning, a middle, and an end; this is the first rule of organization. This scheme certainly is not new, but many writers have found it extremely useful and the rule has survived.

One reason for the wide acceptance is that the three parts offer an easy framework within which to write. In a report on a research project, for example, the writer can give background information on the project before he discusses the procedure he followed. He can present the results before he draws his conclusions and makes any recommendations. This is the way he would tell the story if he were left to his own designs. The order is straightforward and he feels comfortable with it.

The scheme also works nicely for reporting information that does not follow a general time base. In analytical reports, the beginning is the premise, the middle is the analysis, and the ending is the synthesis. In reports describing a new device or concept, the beginning is the overview, the middle is the presentation of details, the ending is the summing up.

Because the three parts represent distinct communication functions, I prefer to call them by the following descriptive names: *the briefing, the evidence,* and *the evaluation.* The standard order in which they appear is represented in Illus. 9–1.

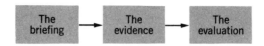

Illus. 9–1. Standard order of the parts of the body of a report.

The briefing constitutes the Introduction. It supplies whatever preliminary information the reader needs in order to understand the evidence. It states the problem and the purpose and defines or explains any existing facts that have a direct bearing on the case (see Chapter 5).

The evidence constitutes the objective reporting of the facts. It is the presentation of the evidence, pro and con, to the jury. Information is "out of order" if it does not bear directly on the premise, as announced in the briefing.

The evaluation constitutes an appraisal of the facts in terms of the purpose that was announced in the briefing. In the analogy of the court of law, it is the summing up by either the prosecution or the defense — depending on which side the writer represents. It may be followed by specific recommendations. (Not all reports have an evaluation section. If his opinion isn't asked for, a writer may decide not to offer any conclusions or recommendations, finishing his report with a short summary of his most important findings and leaving the reader to draw his own conclusions. Or a report may simply supply the data for a particular use and no evaluation of the data may be necessary.)

Modification of the standard order is sometimes desirable. If the writer knows that his reader will be interested mainly in the evaluation, he might move that part into the middle position, forming an integrated unit with the briefing (see Illus. 9–2).

Illus. 9–2. Modification of the standard order.

Moving the evaluation into the first position, ahead of the briefing, is another possibility, but poses a danger. The writer has to be sure that sufficient introductory material is provided either in a foreword or letter of transmittal, or in the abstract. I have seen this modification used with moderate success in a few reports, but in each the need could have been met more efficiently if the writer had concentrated on providing a good informative abstract.

INTERNAL ORGANIZATION OF THE PARTS

Thomas Mann maintained that order and simplification are the first steps toward the mastery of a subject. He may not have had technical writing in mind when he said this, but I'm sure he would have agreed that the association is appropriate.

Once a reader begins a report, he looks for signs to tell him how the parts are organized. If there is a table of contents, it will give him a quick map of where he is going. Then the in-text headings and subheadings take over. They tell him where he is along the route and what is to come; they show him what material is primary, what is secondary, and how the parts are related; they provide transition; they help control the pace; they act as reference markers; and they add variety to the format. The following exhibit demonstrates how descriptive headings and subheadings help the writer achieve an orderly presentation.

Functional parts	Headings used in report
The Title	SELECTION OF CONTROL SYSTEMS FOR SPACE VEHICLES
The briefing (2 pages)	I. INTRODUCTION A. Problems of stabilization and attitude control B. Criteria for selecting control systems
The evidence (18 pages)	II. STABILIZATION SYSTEMS A. Gravitational-gradient stabilization B. Aerodynamic stabilization C. Radiation pressure stabilization D. Spin stabilization E. Comparison of stabilization systems III. ATTITUDE CONTROL SYSTEMS A. Control using gyros B. Control utilizing the earth's magnetic field C. Control using inertia wheels D. Control using reaction jets E. Control using reaction spheres F. Moving-mass attitude control G. Control by earth scanning H. Control by star or planet tracking I. Control using combined systems
The evaluation (2 pages)	IV. GENERAL EVALUATION V. RECOMMENDED AREAS FOR FURTHER STUDY

The exhibit also shows that (1) the presentation of evidence generally is much longer than the briefing or the evaluation, (2) each of the three functional parts, designated at the left, may contain more than one section, and (3) a carefully prepared outline could supply most of the headings and subheadings for a report.

Applying the three-part scheme to the organization of a report on a simple experimental investigation, we can assign the following general headings and subheadings to the body. (In an actual report, of course, the author would substitute words that describe the subject matter he is dealing with.)

Specimen Headings for a Report on an Experiment

INTRODUCTION
Statement of problem
Statement of purpose

THEORETICAL ANALYSIS
Assumptions
Calculations

EXPERIMENTAL WORK
General procedure
Facilities and equipment
Tests
Results of tests

DISCUSSION OF RESULTS
Comparison of theoretical
   and experimental results
Conclusion

HOW TO HANDLE A TECHNICAL DESCRIPTION

Technical descriptions are difficult to write, but there are reliable rules to follow in planning the overall configuration. The most important of these is *to present the whole before the parts*. In describing a new concept, a new device, or a new procedure, discuss the essence, the function, the purpose of the concept, device, or procedure — considered as a whole — before confronting the reader with the details.

I received a student report several years ago entitled "The Step-Down Detector." I was familiar with many types of detectors, but had never heard of this one and had no mental picture of what to expect. The report began with a list of equipment, followed by a circuit schematic. On page 3 I found this statement: "The step-down detector is a portable device to aid the blind. Basically, it consists of a light source, a photoelectric sensing element, and an alarm circuit that warns the carrier of the device that he is approaching a step down." If I had had this statement on page 1, I would not have wasted valuable reading time trying to guess the meaning of "step-down."

As you may have realized, not only does the whole-before-the-parts scheme meet an important psychological need of every reader, but it also promotes sound structural organization. At the paragraph level, the whole becomes the topic sentence; at the section level, it becomes the introductory paragraph. And at the report level, it becomes the informative abstract.

Other important rules that will guide you in planning an effective technical description are:

1. Make sure that the manner in which the parts are organized is immediately apparent to the reader.

2. Try always to proceed from the familiar to the unfamiliar. Establish a common ground with the reader, either by direct reference or by analogy.

3. Determine whether your verbal description of "the whole" would not be improved by the addition of a block diagram.

4. Check the pace. The most common mistake is to overcrowd sentences and paragraphs (see Chapter 8).

PUTTING THE PARTS IN ORDER

Look at a checkerboard in one light and you see black squares on red; in another light, red squares on black. From one angle, you may see columns running front to back; from another, rows running side to side or diagonally. Many patterns can emerge from a single graphic design.

So it is with a piece of writing. The writer might describe a device or a circuit in such a way that the reader sees a different pattern from the one intended. Or perhaps the picture is vague and a fuzzy pattern emerges.

No single way of assembling the bits and pieces of a technical description is "best" for all situations. The writer has to anticipate the angle from which the reader will view his writing and analyze the light in which it will be interpreted. Only through careful analysis of the subject and the reader can he determine what the best structure for the parts is.

The structural designs available to you as a technical writer are:

1. Expanded definition	5. Enumeration
2. Time relation	6. Cause and effect
3. Space relation	7. Comparison and contrast
4. Logical sequence	8. Classification or partition

Your first task is to select the design that will accommodate the subject matter and the audience you are to deal with. All designs should be given a chance to qualify. Sometimes a combination works best. Or sometimes the subject matter itself dictates your choice of design.

Once you have selected a design, you must then decide which pattern will be most likely to convey your thoughts successfully. Each design, like the checkerboard, offers alternative patterns; you should investigate all possibilities before deciding on one. Here are a few questions you should ask yourself before you begin to use any of the designs listed.

In an expanded definition, should you begin with the term or idea to be defined and then point out its distinguishing features, or should you begin with the features and lead up to the term or idea?

In a time relation, should you arrange your ideas from the past to the present, from the present to the past, or from present to past to present by a series of flashbacks?

In a space relation, should you go from right to left or from left to right? From top to bottom or from bottom to top? From inside to outside or from outside to inside?

In a logical sequence, should you proceed from input to output or from output back to input? Should you list the most important item first or last in a series based on order of importance?

In an enumeration, should you list items in the order of occurrence, order of importance, or order of familiarity?

In a causal relation, should you report the cause and then the effect, or the effect and then the cause?

In a comparison, should you develop a parallel comparison a step at a time or should you present one of the items in its entirety before beginning the comparison?

In a classification scheme, should you group by structure, by principle of operation, by function, by cost, by weight, by size, by power, or by some other characteristic?

These questions show the many patterns available to you, the writer. But unless the design has been set for you, you must make the choice. If you are willing to experiment, to try alternative methods before settling on one, you will see definite improvement in your ability to communicate. The time spent experimenting will thus pay you dividends in clarity.

Postscript: Volta Torrey, past publisher of the M.I.T. alumni magazine, *Technology Review,* and former editor of *Popular Science,* compares the reader's experience in beginning to read a technical report with the experience of a man entering a maze. Both are on their own in strange surroundings and both can easily be misled and become bewildered. The difference, of course, is that a maze is intended to confuse; it isn't considered much of a maze if it doesn't. A report, on the other hand, is intended to enlighten; it isn't considered much of a report if it doesn't.

So far as I know, no prize is being offered to the author of the best literary maze of the year. But there still are many competitors. Their point in common: an ability to mislead without even trying.

10

Read over your compositions, and

when you meet with a passage you

think is particularly fine, strike it out.

SAMUEL JOHNSON

THE ARBITRARY EDITOR

All of us, whether we realize it or not, are editors. Perhaps not *good* editors, but editors nevertheless. Every time we read over something we have written we become editors; every time we change a word or add a phrase we are editing.

Editing one's own writing is an essential step in improving the quality of a report. But it is only a first step; an independent judgment by a third party can help even more — provided that party knows his business and is not an arbitrary critic.

Some organizations hire professional editors to handle the editing of all formal reports. Others, especially in research and development, prefer to have their technical supervisors serve part time as editors. Whether one system or the other is better depends entirely on local demands and conditions, but there is nothing in his training or background that automatically prevents a technical person from becoming an effective editor. He does need a chance to prepare himself for the role, however.

If you are a technical supervisor (or are about to become one) and are faced with the added responsibility of editing the reports your engineers or scientists write, you've probably wondered how you can handle the job more efficiently. Perhaps editing is a new field for you, posing many problems of procedure, policy, or technique. And perhaps you feel a bit uncertain about the way you've met some of these problems. In any event, an opportunity to check your standards against those of others might be both reassuring and profitable. This chapter is a collection of the common guideposts that many professional editors have found useful in developing a rapport with engineer-writers. Although it is addressed to the part-time editor, it should also serve, by implication, to acquaint the writer with his responsibilities. (An exhibit of a manuscript before and after editing is given in Appendix II.)

PRIMARY FUNCTIONS OF AN EDITOR

Your primary function as an editor is to guarantee that the reports your engineers write meet certain standards of content, organization, style, and format. Your goal is undeniably clear. How to accomplish the feat is your major problem.

You cannot succeed, of course, unless your writers know what the standards are. So your first task is to acquaint them with the ground rules by issuing general specifications for each type of report your company or department uses. But this is merely a necessary formality. Your main duty is to instill a genuine desire for self-improvement and then provide as much help as you can along the way.

Stimulate Interest

If you have the dual role of technical supervisor and editor you have a better-than-average opportunity to stimulate writer interest. You have daily contact with your men on technical matters and you can tie their writing directly to their research or engineering. This gives you a definite advantage over the editor who does not have a formal technical background, or the one who edits full time.

Interest is contagious. At the outset, be enthusiastic about the importance of good writing. Tell your new engineers how your organization uses its technical reports, how much the reports cost in man-hours and cash, who the readers are, and how much they rely on the reports. Point out that clear, precise reports could help them earn a raise in salary, and ask your director to tell each new group why the company is interested in helping its engineers and scientists become good writers.

Since every writer has a certain amount of mental and physical inertia to overcome, you should make the writing job as straightforward as possible. Many factors are under your control: you can assign the report early in the project, you can allow a realistic time for its completion, you can see to it that the draft an author submits for editing is returned promptly, and you can be sure that he has secretarial help and up-to-date reference books. And finally, you can give him some privacy. He needs a quiet place to do creative work; help him find it.

An equally obvious way to stimulate interest, yet one too frequently ignored, is to praise a job well done. Don't be known only for your criticisms. It is indeed rare that a report does not have some feature worth praising. When you hold an editorial conference, put the author at ease by starting your discussion with a word of encouragement. Later, if the published report has been well received, make a point of mentioning it at the next meeting of your project group.

Along with praise, offer a friendly ear. Being a good listener, *within reasonable limits,* has its advantages: you gain the respect of your writers and establish them as the key participants. Because they feel that the major part of the burden rests on them, they will work harder, and eventually will require less help from you.

Nearly every writer likes to see his name in print. Perhaps certain reports that your organization issues do not carry by-lines. If there is no strong reason for omitting the author's name, or if the original reason is no longer valid, try to have the policy changed. Most of us write more carefully when we have to sign our names to what we say.

CHECK YOUR TECHNIQUE

Once you begin to criticize a piece of writing, you immediately put the author on the defensive. You are attacking his "baby," and you should do so with diplomacy.

Here are some practical suggestions for improving your technique:

1. *Require an outline.* Persuade your writers to produce an outline before they begin to write. Don't be petty about the form, but have them include enough details so that you can evaluate the intended coverage and organization of the report. Afterward, discuss your ideas in an editorial conference. The writer should not go ahead with the job until the two of you agree on the outline. Some writers will complain that an outline involves extra work; your rebuttal is that a review of the outline constitutes a pre-editing of the report and actually saves work.

2. *Refuse a rough draft.* The manuscript that the author sends to you for editing should represent his best effort. You fight a losing battle if you allow him to become careless. Demand clean, pre-edited copy.

3. *Do not revise for the author.* Most editors agree that it often would be easier for them to rewrite an entire report than to get the author to revise it properly. But the mistakes are the author's and he should do the revising; otherwise he will make the same types of errors in his next report. You are doing neither the author or yourself a favor if you fail to hold this line of responsibility.

4. *Spell out your criticisms.* You must be specific when you criticize someone else's writing. General comments such as "not clear" or "you can do better than this" do not help the author with his revisions. Pinpoint what is not clear and then suggest a plan of attack. If you take the time to give detailed comments, the author will be more inclined to view your criticism as constructive.

5. *Be prepared to justify your stand.* Decisions to have an author revise his writing must not be made arbitrarily. You might not say something the way he does, but this is not sufficient reason for him to change his way. You are the boss, nevertheless, and if he violates any of the rules of good writing, good taste, or company policy, you have every right to call these violations to his attention. If he doubts your judgment, justify it by referring him to an accepted authority. Many organizations have published their own style manuals to serve this purpose.

6. *Spare the blue pencil.* Probably nothing is more discouraging to an author than to receive his manuscript covered from beginning to end with an editor's scratchings. Never cross out entire sections or pages; if you haven't

space in the margin for your comments, prepare a separate comment sheet and cross-reference it to the text by numbering the references in sequence. Some editors use a preprinted form that can be filled in quickly and neatly as they edit. A specimen form is included at the end of the chapter, as well as a check list of what to look for when editing.

7. *Stress the major errors.* All your criticisms will not be of equal importance. Assign top priority to any error that threatens clarity, such as poor organization of thought or inadequate background material. Relegate to a secondary role most errors in spelling, punctuation, and mechanics; in other words, don't be a nitpicker.

8. *Confer with the author.* After the author has had a chance to look over your written comments, arrange for an editorial conference. More can be taught in an informal, face-to-face session than by any other method. For example, in discussing a passage that isn't clear, let the author tell you in his own words what he meant. The chances are good that he will produce a satisfactory on-the-spot revision.

9. *Be an impartial critic.* Always be consistent in your judgments: what is wrong for one author, under given conditions, cannot be right for another. This doesn't mean that you can't adopt new rules and modify old ones. But while a rule is "on the books," hold to it. As a practical matter, you would be wise to start with a few major rules and add to them only as experience dictates. Get together with the other supervisors in your department and compare notes. Consistency on this broader level also is important.

10. *Assume full responsibility.* There can be several reviewers of a report but there must be only one editor. Any multiple-editor scheme is inefficient, costly, and ineffective. It results in buck-passing and name-calling. How can you change it? Perhaps you can't, but at least try. The best time is when you are asked to take on the editing job; the next best is when the company reviews its reporting structure and asks for your comments.

CHECK YOUR ATTITUDE

Many of your problems as editor will be psychological. You must develop empathy with your writers without becoming so involved with them personally that you lose perspective. You must consider their needs while serving the best interests of your employer; you must see their point of view while insisting that they satisfy the needs of the reader. And you must somehow see that the responsibility you have to protect your career dovetails with all your "additional" responsibilities.

Avoiding a negative attitude toward editing is not easy, but there can be little compromise. Good editors are bound to spend a harassed existence. Their job requires more than an ability to recognize and to repair poorly constructed manuscripts. To do a good job, an editor must also be a salesman, a teacher, a diplomat, a psychologist, and at times even a chaplain.

No single method of editing is superior. Each of you must use whatever techniques are best suited to the circumstances under which you operate. Just don't get into a rut when you criticize someone else's writing. You are dealing with a precious commodity and it deserves your best talent.

EDITOR'S CHECK LIST

Your job of editing a manuscript should be divided into two parts: commenting on the coverage and organization of the report, and criticizing the writing. This check list suggests a plan of attack. It also raises pertinent questions to guide you in phrasing the comments you might wish to include in a writer's check list such as the one following this exhibit.

Part I: The Coverage and Organization

Read the report through at your normal reading rate to see if the pieces of the story fit together smoothly, then ask yourself the following questions. Base your answers on what you know of the intended reader's needs.

1. Is the thesis of the report clear? If the report does not present a conclusion, is the central idea clear?
2. Is the problem defined? The purpose stated?
3. Are all questions answered? Are answers easily found?
4. Are all elements (Abstract, Introduction, etc.) included as required by the standard format of the organization publishing the report?
5. Is the material presented in an order best suited to the reader's needs?
6. Should material be added? Removed?
7. Are any sections contradictory?
8. Are there enough headings? Effectively worded?
9. Are there enough visual aids? Properly located? Properly referenced?
10. Is the title too general? Vague? Wordy?
11. Is appendix material essential? If so, is it referred to in text and keyed back to text?
12. Is the pace adjusted to fit the subject matter and the reader's knowledge?

13. Is classified or proprietary information included? If so, is it properly identified?
14. If several authors have contributed, are their mechanics of format and organization compatible? Consistent?

Part II: The Writing

Reread the report critically for errors in composition. You will find that they fall into three general categories: errors at the paragraph level, at the sentence level, and at the word level. Some of these errors will be one-of-a-kind; others will be recurring. Your job is to catch *all* errors, but to correct only one of a type to show the author how it's done. The following questions should help you in preparing your comments.

Paragraph organization
1. Do all paragraphs have a topic sentence?
2. Is the topic sentence near the beginning?
3. Do all paragraphs have unity (one topic)?
4. Do all paragraphs have smooth transitions?
5. Should any paragraphs be combined?
6. Should any paragraph be divided into two or more paragraphs?

Sentence structure
1. Are sentences straightforward? Primary information in primary grammatical construction; secondary in subordinate?
2. Are subjects and verbs immediately apparent?
3. Is the information so paced that reader does not have to stop or to reread for meaning?
4. Are sentences punctuated properly? (Comma after long introductory clause or phrase; commas around nonrestrictive clause; comma to prevent run-on; hyphens between parts of compound adjectives.)
5. Has the writer avoided: dangling modifier, misplaced modifier, incomplete comparison, nonparallel construction, disagreement between subject and verb or between pronoun and antecedent?

Word choice
1. Has the writer used a complex or formal word where a simple word would do?
2. Has he used abstract words for concrete ones?
3. Has he used unfamiliar words for familiar ones?

4. Has he avoided vague pronouns?
5. Has he overlooked deadwood (superfluous words, roundabout expressions)?
6. Is there any noticeable redundancy?
7. Are there meaningless or inexact qualifiers?
8. Did he sprinkle his report with jargon? Slang? Clichés?
9. Did he use nonstandard abbreviations?
10. Are there examples of inconsistent wording (names, titles, symbols)?

WRITER'S CHECK LIST

The main reason for using a writer's check list in reporting your editorial comments is to present a neat, orderly account. You avoid cluttering the manuscript and have more room to spell things out. Also, if you use a carbon, you will then have a copy for your records.

A specimen form is given on the facing page. Each comment is keyed to the manuscript by a reference number. Except for their separation into two main categories, entries follow the order in which they occur in the text. Short, routine comments, such as correcting spelling mistakes and punctuation errors, are made on the manuscript itself.

Comments may be continued on the back of the check-list sheet if more room is needed.

SPECIMEN WRITER'S CHECK LIST

Author _J. D. Cowan_ Date ms. received _5/9_ Conference date _5/12_

Title of report _Modified Computer Network for the Tactical Air Control Weather Facility_

The Coverage and Organization

Ref. in ms.	Comment
1	Your introduction does not give the reader sufficient briefing on the history of the project. Begin when the Air Force took over from ONR.
4	This step appears to be out of sequence. Why insert here? Move to page 7, para 3? Or to page 8 as last para?
8	The material on pages 9 and 10 is not primary material. Why not move to an appendix? (At the top of P-9 you say that the material "is of limited interest.")

The Writing

Ref. in ms.	Comment
2	Sentence much too long to open a discussion. Take it easy on the reader. He's new to the game!
3	The pace is much too rapid here. Remember, the reader has never heard of the system before. Suggest several sentences + a new subheading.
5	Paragraph trouble. This technical description is difficult to follow. Don't compound the difficulty by crowding into one paragraph. Break after "computer".
6	Define this new term. Spell out first, then abbreviate.
7	No reference in text to this figure.

APPENDIX I

AN ANNOTATED BIBLIOGRAPHY

PRIMARY REFERENCES

1. Technical Writing

FEDERAL ELECTRIC CORPORATION, *How to Write Effective Reports*. Reading, Mass.: Addison-Wesley, 1965. The only commercially available programmed book on the subject. Self-instruction feature offers especially good sections on format, mechanics, and presentation of data.

HAYS, ROBERT, *Principles of Technical Writing*. Reading, Mass.: Addison-Wesley, 1965. Concentrates on helping beginning writers, even those without a flair for writing clear reports. Designed as a text for a one-quarter or a one-semester course in technical writing. Text gives examples of both good and bad practice.

ULMAN, JOSEPH N., and JAY R. GOULD, *Technical Reporting*, revised edition. New York: Henry Holt, 1959. One of the most popular and usable of the many textbooks on technical writing. Easy reference handbook arrangement; many "before and after" examples.

2. Scientific and Engineering Writing

GILMAN, WILLIAM, *The Language of Science*. New York: Harcourt, Brace, and World, 1961. An excellent treatment of uses and abuses of the language. Contains many verbal examples and is written with life and humor. The book itself is a model of good prose.

RATHBONE, ROBERT R., and JAMES B. STONE, *A Writer's Guide for Engineers and Scientists*. Englewood Cliffs, N.J.: Prentice-Hall, 1962. May be used as a classroom text, a self-help text, or a reference. Analyzes the major problems technical people face in writing reports; offers specimen reports to show how these problems are solved. Typical chapters: "Reporting Negative Results," "Achieving the Proper Pace," "Satisfying the Reader's Needs."

ROSENSTEIN, ALAN B., ROBERT R. RATHBONE, and WILLIAM SCHNEERER, *Engineering Communications*. Englewood Cliffs, N.J.: Prentice-Hall, 1964. The only book that combines theory and practice: the first part covers communication theory; the second and third parts relate the theory directly to oral and written communication and to graphics. One of the Prentice-Hall series on engineering design. Paperback or hardback.

3. English Usage

EVANS, BERGEN, and CORNELIA EVANS, *A Dictionary of Contemporary English Usage.* New York: Random House, 1957. Deals with both American and British usage, but from the viewpoint of the American writer or speaker. Examples selected from everyday writing and speech; word preferences, grammar, style, punctuation, and idioms are discussed.

FOWLER, H. W., *Modern English Usage.* New York: Oxford University Press; first edition, 1926, revised edition, 1965, edited by Sir Ernest Gowers. The most famous and influential book on English usage; written with gusto and witty erudition. Particularly recommended are: "Formal Words," "Avoidance of the Obvious," "Elegant Variation," "Haziness," "Love of the Long Word." Hardback.

PERRIN, PORTER G., *Writer's Guide and Index to English,* third edition. Chicago: Scott, Foresman, 1959. A standard handbook for any kind of writer. Part I, "The Writer's Guide," has thorough discussions of style, grammar, punctuation, usage, and mechanics. Part II, "The Index to English," is an alphabetical arrangement of the subjects in Part I. More of an everyday book than the Fowler.

4. Dictionaries

Chambers's Technical Dictionary, edited by C. F. Tweney and L. E. C. Hughes. New York: Macmillan, 1953. Covers the fields of pure and applied sciences and all branches of engineering, construction, and skilled trades. Desk size hardback. Satisfactory for general coverage.

Webster's Seventh New Collegiate Dictionary. Springfield, Mass.: G. & C. Merriam Co., 1963. Based on Webster's New International Dictionary, third edition. Still the best desk dictionary available. In addition to the spelling, pronunciation, etymology, syllabic division, and variant forms, this dictionary gives hyphenation, capitalization, abbreviations, punctuation, signs and symbols, gazetteer, and biographical names. Hardback only.

5. Graphics

CARROL, P., *How to Chart.* New York: McGraw-Hill, 1960. Careful treatment, presented from the writer's point of view. Concise and sensitive suggestions for solutions to the writer's problems in handling graphic materials and methods.

SCHMID, C. S., *Handbook of Graphic Presentation.* New York: Ronald Press, 1954. Exhaustive treatment of the traditional use of graphics. Technique-oriented, thus excellent for setting standards.

VAN HAGEN, C. E., *Report Writer's Handbook.* Englewood Cliffs, N.J.: Prentice-Hall, 1961. Good one-stop shopping. Contains helpful summary of the criteria for selecting graphic techniques (Sections 4–2 and 4–3).

6. Oral Reporting

BRYANT, DONALD C., and KARL R. WALLACE, *Oral Communication,* third revised edition. New York: Appleton-Century-Crofts, 1962. A short course in public speaking. Full coverage on getting started right, amplifying and organizing ideas, developing good style and delivery, group discussions.

WEISS, HAROLD, and J. B. McGRATH, JR., *Technically Speaking.* New York: McGraw-Hill, 1963. Everything the technical person needs on the basic principles of oral reporting. Examples from engineering and scientific subjects. Good reference and self-help guide.

7. Technical Editing

WEIL, B. H. (editor), *Technical Editing.* New York: Reinhold Publishing Company, 1958. Nineteen articles, each by an authority, that together cover the field.

SUPPLEMENTARY REFERENCES

1. Proposal Writing

MANDEL, SIEGFRIED, and DAVID L. CALDWELL, *Proposal and Inquiry Writing.* New York: Macmillan, 1962. A good "first book" on proposal writing. Analysis of the structure, content, and language of proposals; descriptions of the procedures and techniques for writing.

2. Grammar

STRUNK, WILLIAM, JR., and E. B. WHITE, *The Elements of Style.* New York: Macmillan, 1959. Originally a composition handbook used at Cornell; revised and added to by E. B. White. Short, to the point, witty, and inexpensive. The only book on grammar and usage that has ever made the best-seller list. Can be read in one evening. Paperback or hardback.

TURNER, RUFUS P., *Grammar Review for Technical Writers.* New York: Holt, Rinehart, and Winston, 1964. Covers the major trouble spots; uses examples from technical writing. Paperback.

3. Titling Technical Reports

CHADBOURNE, H. L., *Titling Technical Reports for Optimum Use and Retrieval.* Inter-laboratory Committee on Editing and Publishing, Monograph 7, West Coast Naval Laboratories, 1965. A 12-page discussion stressing the need for better, more informative titles and showing how to achieve them. Well written, nicely illustrated. May be obtained free by writing to Technical Information Division (Code 23), U. S. Naval Ordnance Laboratory, Corona, California 91720.

4. Communicating with Management

Readings in Communication, from *Fortune,* edited by Francis William Weeks. New York: Holt, Rinehart, and Winston, 1961. An entertaining and revealing collection of articles on information theory, business communications, brainstorming, panel discussions, human relations, oral presentations, all written by experts in the various fields. Paperback.

5. Writing About Science for the Layman

EMBERGER, META RILEY, and MARIAN HALL, *Scientific Writing*. New York: Harcourt, Brace, 1955. Emphasizes the fundamentals of writing technical material for the non-technical reader.

The following articles are recommended by Volta Torrey, past publisher of M.I.T.'s *Technology Review* and one-time editor of *Popular Science:*

"Writing General Science Articles," by Gerard Piel (publisher of *Scientific American*), *J. Chem. Educ.*, January 1954.

"The Three Ages of Science Writing," by Lawrence Lessing, *Chemical and Engineering News*, May 1963, **41**, p. 78.

"Scientific Explanation," by Warren Weaver, *Science*, March 20, 1964, **143**, 3612, p. 1297.

6. Journal Articles

Most of the professional technical societies have compiled handbooks and style guides for would-be authors of journal articles. These are available free or at small cost. Do not submit a manuscript without first consulting the appropriate guide. The American Standards Association (10 East 40th St., New York, N.Y.) has several helpful bulletins for the technical writer; in particular, inspect their bulletin on abbreviations of scientific and engineering terms.

7. Fun-to-Read Pieces About Writing

EHRENFRIED, ALBERT D. *How to Write Technical Reports and Still Maintain Your Sanity*. A private publication issued by Technical Marketing Associates of Concord, Massachusetts, and available from them at a small charge. Contains sound advice for the technical person on how to avoid some of the major pitfalls in report-writing. Pamphlet.

MASTERSON, JAMES R., and WENDELL BROOKS PHILLIPS, *Federal Prose, or How to Write in and/or for Washington*. Chapel Hill: The University of North Carolina Press, 1948. To quote the publisher: "Trained in English at Harvard, the authors entered the Government service from patriotic motives — only to discover that their training was incompetent, irrelevant, and immaterial. Nothing baffled, they extirpated the out-moded English language from their thought patterns and mastered the intricacies of Federal Prose. Theirs the agony, yours the gain." Paperback (but hard to find these days).

Space for Additional References You May Wish to Remember

1. _____

2. _____

3. _____

4. _____

5. _____

6. _____

APPENDIX II

A JOURNAL ARTICLE
BEFORE AND AFTER EDITORIAL REVISION

This exhibit demonstrates how much we can improve clarity and readability if we are willing to spend some extra time revising a manuscript. (Our words somehow look different to us after we stay away from them for awhile and come back fresh.) The general organization of the original was not changed, but the paragraphing was tightened, as you will see. The greatest improvements the author made were: (1) He replaced abstract words with concrete words, the passive voice with the active, and clichés with meaningful terms. (2) He eliminated many wordy phrases and awkward constructions. (3) He subordinated secondary ideas. To help you cross check, I have underlined some of the offenders that the author changed. Undoubtedly you will see others that you believe he should have changed. Both specimens were supplied by the technical information department of a large manufacturer.

ORIGINAL DRAFT	PUBLISHED VERSION
Title: *Better Management*	Title: *Better Management Information Systems*

Whatever else we say about the opportunities and problems that will present themselves in 1963, we can be sure that a large part of them will take on a considerably different guise than those we have experienced in the past.	Opportunities for applying management information systems will increase rapidly in 1963, largely due to the growing severity of business problems that have already arrived.
In both the product producing and service industries, there will be continued and increasing pressure for better profits, productivity, and vol-	In both the product-producing and service industries, there will be continued and increasing pressure for better profits, productivity and volume — all necessary to maintain and improve stockholder interest. These

ume — all necessary to maintain and improve the stockholders' interest. And this has to be done in the face of militant competition from national and international sources. It seems evident that the problem is compounded in many businesses by soft prices resulting primarily from excess capacity, and the effects of foreign competitive efforts.

This is a very dynamic situation which gives renewed emphasis to the importance and value of information systems for management control. For it is in this climate of stringency that general management is most willing to turn to new concepts and techniques which will improve their competitive position.

The American Management Association, in its role as an educator, has as one of its prime missions the origination, development and dissemination of information and technology which will help accomplish the job at hand.

The Association is keenly aware of the contribution it can make to its members by freely exchanging the most advanced concepts as well as proven developments in management administration. Illustratively, over the past few years, we have seen continued stress being put on conventional work measurement and methods studies as the prelude to more advanced systems design; the emergence of the administrative management concept involving the total

improvements must be made in the face of militant competition—both domestic and foreign. The problem is compounded in many businesses by soft prices that have resulted from the effects of excess capacity and foreign competition.

This dynamic situation emphasizes the importance and value of information systems for management control. In a climate of stringency, general management is willing and anxious to investigate new concepts and techniques that can improve their competitive situation. To this end, American Management Assn., in its role as an educator, originates, develops and disseminates helpful information and technology.

The Association freely exchanges with its members the most advanced concepts as well as proven developments in management administration. For example, in recent years we have seen continued emphasis on conventional work measurement and methods studies as a prelude to more advanced systems design; the administrative management concept has emerged, with its emphasis on the total information system as differentiated from the management of indi-

information system as differentiated from the management of individual clerical efforts; and the practical application of analytical control techniques such as PERT (time/cost) for better management decision making. In 1963, there will be an enlarged effort to present these and other concepts to management for their evaluation and application. There seems to be little question that a wider range of usage can be anticipated.

Many managements are beginning to be appreciative of the potential improvements available from an investment in information systems work; and, while there were some early mistakes that have been largely overcome, the degree of understanding from a conceptual standpoint is starting to catch up with the capabilities of the equipment to process the information. Systems designers are becoming more proficient, and management is beginning to understand what the systems designers are talking about even though the educational process has a long way to go.

Hardware developments in the coming year will become more concerned with molecularization, thin films, tunnel diodes, true parallel processors rather than time sharing, and the advances being publicized in the fields of cryogenics, optics, pneumatics, as well as other gaseous systems, and hydraulics.

vidual clerical efforts; and analytical control techniques, such as PERT (time/cost), have been applied to aid management decision making. In 1963, there will be an enlarged effort to present these and other concepts to management for their evaluation and application. We anticipate an expanding range of acceptance of these advanced concepts.

Many managements are beginning to appreciate the potential improvements made possible by an investment in information systems work. Some early mistakes have been largely overcome, and the degree of understanding from a conceptual standpoint is starting to catch up with the capabilities of information processing equipment. Systems designers are becoming more proficient, and management is beginning to understand what the systems designers are talking about—even though the educational process has a long way to go.

Designers of computer equipment will become more concerned with advancing technological developments — molecularization, thin films, tunnel diodes, and true parallel processors rather than time-sharing techniques. However, there will be relatively little practical application of these developments this year. Although speeds,

However, there will be relatively little practical application during 1963; and computer equipments, although there will be changes in speeds, configurations, and new control methods, will be pretty much as we know them today.

Software, on the other hand, could very well experience some changes that could border on a technological breakthrough. This, in turn, could have a very beneficial effect on systems design and the efficiency with which information systems can be produced and operated. COBOL will undoubtedly gain greater acceptance for documentation and modular programming with a by-product of easing management's understanding of the process involved.

As information systems design progresses during the year, it would appear that the time cycle related to closing the loop (i.e., feedback of change to previously established plans or instructions) will become more and more important to the information cycle, whether it be concerned with a factory location or at the other end of the scale, a clerical service operation. Indicative of progress in this area is the fact that there are many large-scale systems being designed today which require electronic feedback devices to make the system efficiently operable. Certainly, we will see and hear a great deal more about this in 1963.

configurations and control methods may improve, basic computer equipment will remain much as we know it today.

However, the techniques of applying this computer equipment could experience changes that border on a technological breakthrough. Programming techniques, such as Cobol, will undoubtedly gain greater acceptance, with the by-product of improving management's understanding of the process involved. This, in turn, could benefit systems design and improve the efficiency of producing and operating information systems.

As information systems become more complex, deviations from established plans or instructions will cause more serious disruptions in systems operation if not detected and corrected immediately. Hence, the time required for detection and feedback of change from established plans becomes more and more important to the information cycle. Many of the large-scale information systems now being designed require high-speed electronic feedback of information to make the system operate efficiently. Certainly, we will see and hear more about this in 1963.

Discussions on the relative merits of centralization vis-a-vis decentralization of information processing will undoubtedly continue and be influenced by developments in hardware, software and data transmission equipment. It is anticipated that the per unit cost of electronic information processing will continue to be reduced, and this cost reducing trend will probably also start to apply to transmitting data and getting it off and on the transmission media. If these trends continue in the case of data processing and start in the case of data transmission, then the centralization vs. decentralization argument will be partially solved, with relatively large businesses being the first to resolve their position and capitalize on the resultant benefits.

The year 1963 should be very formative and dynamic for those of us concerned with productivity improvement. As a gentle admonition, let us not forget as we are exploiting the opportunities that will be presented to us that we must anticipate and minimize the human impacts involved. We must also educate, for this is the basis of understanding and progress.

We are only limited by the extent and magnitude of our imagination as applied in a practical manner.

Discussion about the relative merits of centralization versus decentralization of information processing will continue, and be influenced by developments in computers, operating techniques, and data transmission equipment. The per-unit cost of electronic information processing should continue to decline; this cost-reducing trend should soon apply to transmitting information, and getting it on and off the transmission media. If these predicted trends hold true, the centralization versus decentralization argument will be partially solved, with relatively large businesses being first to resolve their position and capitalize on the resultant benefits.

This year should be formulative and dynamic for those of us concerned with productivity improvement. As a gentle admonition, let us not forget that, as we exploit the opportunities of management information systems, we must anticipate and minimize the human impacts involved. We must also educate, for this is the basis of understanding and progress. Our progress is limited only by the extent and magnitude of our imagination as applied in a practical manner.

INDEX

THE AUTHOR

Robert R. Rathbone is an Associate Professor of English in the Department of Humanities at the Massachusetts Institute of Technology. Here he conducts technical reporting and thesis preparation courses and writing seminars for the Aeronautics, Civil Engineering, Electrical Engineering, Mechanical Engineering, and Metallurgy Departments.

For several years he has been the director of special M.I.T. summer programs on writing and editing scientific and industrial reports, and has taught similar programs at the University of California at Los Angeles.

Professor Rathbone has had wide experience as a technical writer. He has also written TV scripts, news releases, journal articles and training films, and is the co-author of two texts: A Writer's Guide for Engineers and Scientists and Engineering Communications.

As an industrial consultant he has conducted in-plant seminars and courses on technical reporting, has organized publication groups, and has served as editorial advisor.

THE BOOK

This book is intended as a primary text for short in-plant writing courses for engineers and scientists, and as a secondary text for college courses in engineering, science, and technical writing. As such, it is designed to serve as an inexpensive self-help reference book for both the student and the professional.

The text concentrates on matters that technical people themselves have found to be the most bothersome in the reports, texts, and articles they read day after day. Coverage includes improving the writing of abstracts, titles, technical descriptions, conclusions, and recommendations. The book also details how to eliminate semantic and mechanical "noise," how to edit someone else's writing, and how to organize subject matter effectively.

An annotated bibliography and helpful references are included, as well as a special chapter on editing, slanted for the technical person. No special preparation is required for an understanding of the material presented.

ADDISON-WESLEY PUBLISHING COMPANY

READING, MASSACHUSETTS

PALO ALTO · LONDON · DON MILLS, ONTARIO